# THE VIRGIN PIG KEEPER

## A Pair of Pigs in the Garden

David Brown FLS

Illustrations by Eric Copeland

**Whittet Books**

Whittet Books Ltd
1 St John's Lane
Stansted
Essex CM24 8JU
email: mail@whittetbooks.com

First published 2010


A catalogue record for this book is available from the British Library.

ISBN 978 1 873580 79 0

Designed by Lodge Graphics

Printed by Cromwell Press Group, Trowbridge, Wiltshire

To Ailsa Brown,
the 'wife of a farmer but not a farmer's wife'.

# CONTENTS

# INTRODUCTION

Meet a socially lively, boisterous, highly intelligent, sexually uninhibited animal with an apparent keen and wicked sense of humour, and which when securely housed is a wonder at reducing human stress. They are also exasperating, loveable, fascinating, profitable in a sane economy and highly addictive.

Winston Churchill with his usual sagacity summed them up.

'Cats', he said, 'look down on you, dogs look up at you, but pigs look you straight in the eye like an equal.'

Rub a pig's back and you get a frank glance which says that you're not alone in the world. P. G. Wodehouse knew a thing or two about human nature and swine when he created the laid back Empress of Blandings, and what other beast but the pig could have become the movers and thinkers of Orwell's *Animal Farm*?

He had them well cast; watch pigs closely and you'll see them stand back, consider and think through their next move. Look long enough at a large group of pigs and you'll see a lot of recognisable human strengths and foibles.

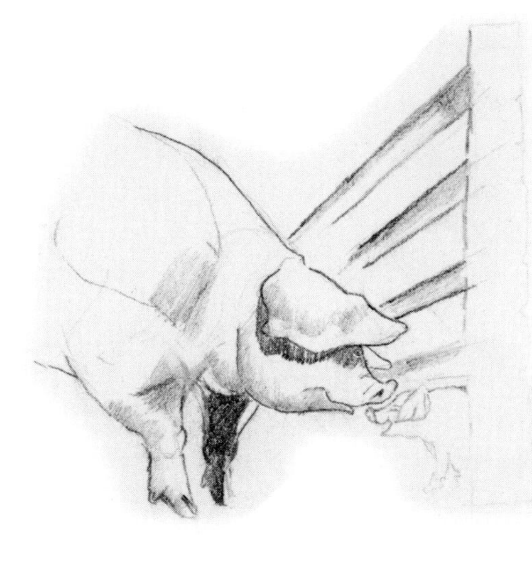

More recently research and experience has shown the remarkably soothing effect of looking after pigs on tough and violent characters in civilian and military prisons.

Pigs seem to have a remarkable fascination for a wide swathe of the human race, as seen by their constant appearance on cards, posters, in children's books, as ornaments and a huge variety of other gifts, tacky and otherwise.

Speak to anyone middle-aged and over who has lived in the countryside; more often than not they will have had some connection with pigs, however remote, and their eyes brighten when they tell you about it. The main reason that pigs were kept by country folk in times past was not for their company, however, but for the compelling reason of keeping hunger at bay during the long bleak winter.

Nowadays, when few of us know real hunger, keeping a pig, apart from producing cheap and delectable meat low in cholesterol, satisfies the squirrel instinct in us by producing this largesse from food which would otherwise be wasted.

Given most people's loss of contact with farming this folk memory of pigs seems doomed. Perhaps not so? It's possible that a new generation will one day be boring their children with nostalgic tales of when their parents kept a pig.

Under the combination of increasingly tedious travel to work, the stress of city life and modern communications many people are now working from home. Before long the largest businesses will have networks of informal workers either working from home or from high-tech rural offices.

Many will then be able to fulfil their dream of living in the country which often brings with it having a bit of land, be it only half an acre. There is also the squirrel instinct brought on by the threat of long-term hard times to come, the desire to batten down the hatches and indulge in self sufficiency.

The 'country' in the broadest sense is also where large numbers of healthy fit people retire. It's often at this point that the idea of keeping livestock and more particularly a pig starts to intrude the subconscious, maybe after reading entertaining self-sufficiency books on a winter's evening. You have a large garden or a half acre of land doing nothing; why not keep a couple of pigs?

The difficulty arises when you start thinking about where to begin. The obvious answer at first glance is to find somewhere to house them, buy a couple of small ones and some food and watch them grow into joints of pork. Alternatively you can buy some expensive textbooks which will get you slowly nowhere because none of them start from ground zero. They tell you what to do but not how. They are all naturally enough written for aspiring or established pig farmers and assume a basic knowledge and intention to keep swine on a scale to keep body and soul together, an ambition not always achieved.

Another way is to ask a professional pig farmer but he will be busy working a twelve hour day trying to avoid going bankrupt. Also he'll be thinking on an entirely different scale. You could offer to work for him free to get some pig know-how which might be interesting for both of you.

Keeping pigs on a small scale should be relatively simple, though that is something no seasoned pig farmer would ever say out loud. As long as you follow the 'do unto others' principle and keep them warm, comfortable and well fed while using affection, a bit of commonsense and acquired know-how, your disasters will be on a small scale.

The problems arise in getting the know-how without it costing you money, and in the complications inherent in our over-regulated society. Time was if you wanted to keep a pig in the garden you just went ahead and did it under the shelter of the Public Health Act 1936, Section 92, where any disputes were judged by the Health and Environment Officer on the basis of how it would affect a reasonable person. He, the reasonable person, is sadly long dead and gone, though if you live in a remote enough area you could perhaps pretend that he lives on. The rest of you had better read the chapter on regulations.

On grants and the European Union, should this cross your mind, don't expect any of the untold billions we pay out to come trickling down to you.

Pigs, unlike most of agriculture, have had no subsidies for many decades, hence no pork and bacon mountain.

So that you know what you're getting, then, this book aims to answer the questions you don't yet know enough to ask and to give you know-how about the sharp end of keeping a pig, like when it's poorly and how to move it from A to B. The book also tells you how to keep the bureaucrats at bay and, if you fancy it, make the best sausages you have ever tasted.

**Notes from a large pig farm**

Every night before bed I pull on my slightly damp wellies and go and walk round the unit.

There are several reasons for this.

If sows are farrowing or due to farrow they need a look and a bit of TLC and sometimes midwifery attention. Also it is always a pleasure to stand and listen to a room full of fulfilled mums feeding and chatting to their offspring.

Walking round the fattening pens a flash of the torch shows if they are warm and comfortable. You are not the only one awake, there are always one or two glassy eyes among the slumbering bodies watching you.

It is useful just to stand and listen – listen for the wrong sound, like the gasping noise of a pig with its head stuck in a railing, or a group setting about another who in their eyes is not politically correct.

One pitch dark night, while I was standing quietly by a six foot wall, I suddenly felt a gentle tap on my shoulder.

My blood froze – until I turned and said 'Hello you' to our large black cat.

# WHERE TO PUT THEM

How to house your pigs naturally comes first but do not spend a penny or move a spadeful of earth until you have read the chapter on regulations, because that will to some degree affect what you put up and where. Irrespective of any regulations, though, always bear in mind that it makes sense to put them as far from any houses as possible and downwind.

Now let's move on to something more elevating; the basics of housing swine. There are two methods of housing pigs on your scale. Either you go for permanent concrete floors and block walls or keep them in mobile runs and huts. The second is generally cheaper and simpler especially as regards regulations, but we'll deal first with some basic thoughts which apply to both.

The first basic law is that any construction needs to be three times as strong as appears necessary and built up as far as a 90 kg pig can reach, say four feet (measurements from now on will be in their most easily understandable form, whether metric or imperial).

You may think this advice is a bit over the top when your first two 30 kg pigs walk hesitantly into their pen and size the place up, but they grow faster as they get bigger and they will test any material to the limit. Pigs are devoured with curiosity from birth and will thoughtfully chew away at all exposed edges and enlarge and alter any crevice or hole they can get their snouts into. This will be done with no ill will, pigs have no malevolence except for a rare few when they get old and crotchety, also a recognisable condition in humans.

Another bit of advice from interesting experience - always make the cement stronger than any advice you get from builders when building block walls. Some builders use cement just to keep the bricks or blocks apart; your walls have to be seriously strong.

Next, pigs need to be able to get and keep warm, cosy and draught-free when there is snow and ice and general inclement weather, and to be able to survive the occasional heat wave in summer.

Keeping them warm is not just an act of civility to your pigs, but also to your pocket. If they're cold they will use most of the energy they get from their food to keep warm and lay on fat. They use a lot of their food on maintenance anyway and the rest on growth, so the more you cut down on their need for maintenance, keeping warm being one of the main factors, the better they will grow.

It must also be obvious to them where to dung and pee, away that is from their bed and eating area. This can become a problem. If the bed area is too hot and stuffy in hot weather they will, logically, sleep outside in the cool and pee on their bed. This can be habit forming and difficult to cure. The chapter on husbandry gives you more information on this.

Most pig buildings are a compromise between the optimum conditions for the pig and ease of working for their attendant humans. In your case with only a few pigs you can swing it strongly their way, though still avoiding, for instance, having to crawl into their bed on hands and knees.

This might be a good point to mention general 'sordidity'. Pig habitations can become seriously disgusting even quicker than a teenager's bedroom. It makes a good impression on possibly critical neighbours if discarded

*...having to crawl into their bed on hands and knees*

baler string, rusty troughs, rotten wood, rubble, collapsed barrows and rampant nettles are kept under control. Clearing such mess away also reduces the available living quarters for unwanted small four-legged beasties.

The next essential is drainage and this you must get right. This applies mostly to permanent buildings. Rainwater once contaminated with pig effluent becomes pig slurry in the eyes of officialdom and getting that in a ditch comes just before serial murder. It's quite easy to separate the two using gutters to take the rainwater and then you and your garden can easily cope with the rich remainder. You could also bring in floor slopes to guide the effluent and, acting on the principle that water seldom runs up hill, keep the bed area at the highest point.

Feeding and drinking come next. You can feed meal or meal in cube form on any dry area. The bed area is ideal as this will persuade them to keep it clean. Or you can use a trough. Troughs on your scale come in three main forms.

An open trough, usually concrete, is difficult to clean out and if you have just one or two pigs it makes it easy for the boss pig to get more than its fair share. Try and avoid the urge to build a magnificent concrete trough, at least until you have had a couple of groups of pigs through and tried all the alternatives.

You could have a free-standing metal trough, of variable length so you can position it anywhere. It's durable enough and easy to clean, but is easily turned over

Then there is a metal or plastic hopper for dry meal or pellets, free standing, if large, or fixed to a wall. This is expensive, and you will only be feeding ad lib pellets for a short period. After this period you will only feed a balancer ration and the rest of their food will be cheaper than meal or free.

Probably the best compromise is a light round metal trough fastened by a metal band to the wall, removable by you but not by the pigs. Have one for each pig and put on opposite sides of the pen at an eating height high enough so they can't shovel gunge into it with their snouts.

Water needs to be clean and in liquid form at all times (not a block of ice in cold weather). Pigs deprived of water often carry on eating meal or pellets and can develop salt poisoning and brain damage.

So, should you put the water near the bed where it's warm? No, because then water will spill and induce unsocial piddling illustrating that nothing is simple in pigs. Similarly if you have an automatic bowl fixed to the wall you can't insulate it right down because they will chew off the insulation! Also remember that any automatic bowl or its feeder tank must by regulation be separated from the mains by a non-return valve.

You can compromise, either putting the automatic bowl in the most sheltered place and/or using the light metal bowl attached to the wall. If the water freezes you can tip the ice out. Don't use the old fashioned round cast iron troughs; much better to grow flowers in them. They are hell to clean and will either give you a hernia or break your foot.

Insulation costs extra but it keeps on working for you every day by saving you money. It encourages better growth and more contented animals with fewer problems. It is quite extraordinary how the use and benefits of insulating have still not reached the remoter practitioners of animal husbandry.

It's a good idea to have an insulated roof, otherwise any heat the pigs

*Problems of 'sordidity'*

generate in cold weather will condense on corrugated iron or asbestos and unfeelingly drip down on them. Make sure that whatever material you use has a sealed surface.

The walls at the sides of the bed area next: If you use concrete blocks, either make a cavity wall or use insulation blocks for at least two courses up.

The bed floor insulation is vital. Do not think in permanent buildings you have to put in foundations and rubble as for a tower block; it's only for a couple of pigs to a maximum of 90 kg and probably only to 60 kg. Starting from the bottom then, a layer of rubble, a couple of inches of concrete, a damp course of heavy-duty polythene, as much insulation as you can afford and as thin a final layer as possible, say one and a half to two inches maximum, of strong concrete.

In spite of not having to carry a baby elephant, it needs to be strong. Pigs' feet are sharp and the area which actually touches the ground is small, hence considerable pounds per square inch. When a grown pig treads on your foot you will remember it. In fact, ancient pig keepers often suffer from a little known and as yet un-registered industrial injury known to the fraternity as pigman's foot.

Other afflictions that dedicated pig keepers suffer from out of all proportion to their numbers are worn out knees (pigs' hard heads being mostly at knee height), deafness and sleeping soundly when they have visitors in for the evening.

To resume, this final thin layer of concrete is heresy to some experts but that final layer all has to be warmed up by pig body heat. The insulation, you will understand, is only needed for the actual bed area, or where you hope the pigs will sleep. Having gone through all that, wood of course is a fantastic insulator and a couple of old doors fixed securely or a wooden floor will happily replace expensive alternatives, though not the damp proof membrane.

Icy draughts: Intelligent though they are it's difficult to train pigs to shut the door after them, and the doorway will admit a lot of cold air in winter. There are three things you can do.

Firstly build or fix a short internal low wall or baffle about three feet high from the door along the side of the bed area. Next put a false roof (made of plywood or hardboard) over the bed resting on this wall at one end, and on this you can store your straw. Thirdly fix a door flap to hang over the door. This last point is not as simple as it sounds, as it has to be flexible

*...ragged and well chewed sacks of times past*

and durable against pigs' teeth. Specially made flaps are available from agricultural merchants, replacing the ragged and well chewed old sack of times past.

It can be quite convenient to have a gate or shutter to shut the pigs into their bed while you clean out or do some job where you don't want to be nibbled or investigated by wet and enquiring noses as you bend over. Do not make it solid though as this will deprive them of air.

The gate into the pen barring them from freedom, however, should be extremely solid, with no projecting bits to gnaw and with a bolt at the bottom and at the top; the bottom being where the pigs will test it. Any sliding bolt should be a heavy galvanised one, not the flimsy sort suitable for garden sheds!

It helps to have this outer gate opening outwards; you can then still get in even if they have pushed a heap of muck and old vegetable stalks up against it. Also it's much easier to drive the pigs in and out of the pen.

Having discussed how to shut out the cold draughts they still need some fresh air, especially in warmer weather. The best way to achieve this is to put a sliding shutter in the two side walls above pig height. As a rough guide, have a shutter eighteen inches by six, made of plywood and adjustable from the outside.

Like us, pigs don't like rain much so you could cover in a permanent outside run quite easily, using corrugated iron or plastic sheets on a wooden frame. By diverting the rainwater this will also cut down the production of dilute slurry. If you really want to spoil them you could hang plastic netting from the roof of the outside run down to the top of the wall in winter to calm the wind on the days it comes straight from Iceland. Just make sure they can't reach it.

Instead of having to start from a green-field site you may be the fortunate owner of old outbuildings, which could save you a lot of effort. Having assured yourself that they won't break too many regulations, having ready-built walls and a roof will save you time and money, but you will still need floor insulation and a false roof to keep off any top draught. Also with a

*...the fortunate owner of old outbuildings*

false roof you are partly proof against sudden weather changes, like a gale and driving rain when you forget to shut the windows.

You may inherit an old cottager's style pig pen. The roof will be un-insulated and the floor probably so, but you now know what to do to bring it up to a reasonable standard. You can put the improved floor on top of the old one, no need to dig it all up, and don't forget the draught wall. If you are lucky the building will face south or south west where all pig buildings should face.

*There are ways to keep your pigs inside an enclosure...*

Another housing alternative, and really the simplest choice, is a mobile hut and run. This is mobile in the sense that if you eventually need to you can drag it on skids with a tractor to fresh ground. It can be a wooden hut and attached hurdle run, where you just shut the pigs in the hut, undo the run, move and reassemble.

Even simpler is the electric fenced run with a simple mobile hut or metal ark in it which a couple of you can drag to a fresh place if it has no floor. The benefits of the moveable shelter and outside run are that you get very little aggro from the planners, there is no cleaning out, the ground is cultivated and fertilised and wooden huts are warm and comfortable.

The qualifications are that you need very light and/or well drained land, pure sand is ideal, else your pigs' sharp feet will turn it into deep mud in wet weather. Also you may not want the ground turned over, though the pigs will love doing it, and remember you and they are out in the open in the winter. If you are on heavier ground and it starts to get like the Somme in winter 1916 you can always shift the lot onto fresh ground, depending on how much you have.

There are two ways to keep your pigs inside an enclosure. One way is a fence with well-hammered posts with the corners strengthened, well-strained heavy duty pig wire fencing and, if you are really determined, a couple of strands of barbed wire. It's expensive, hard work and most importantly, not portable.

A much easier way is an electric fence, but you will need to persuade your pigs as to its advantages. If you leave them to find out for themselves they might be startled enough to go right through it, so it's best to show them.

Firstly it is essential to have a non-electrified gate into the run because once trained they won't cross the line of an electric fence even if you remove it.

Put them through the gate and before they start galloping about give them some food just by and under the wire. It's only twelve volts but once they have brushed an ear or damp nose against the wire they will treat it with wariness, while they will still be willing to go out of the gate if required.

As the pigs grow bigger you can use just two wires, but at the initial 30 kg stage it would be best to use sheep/lamb electric fence, four inch squares of what looks like orange baler string on white nylon supports. Put it up just inside the two wires for bigger pigs, then take it away as they get bigger. Do make sure though that the wire is working first or you will just be teaching them to ignore it.

A final word on housing the pig: That great man Cobbet as usual had the last word:

'When I make up my hog's lodging place for the winter', he says, 'I look well at it and consider, whether, upon a pinch, I could, for once in a way, make shift to lodge in it myself. If I shiver at the thought, the place is not good enough for my hogs.'

Says it all really.

Chris is a lovely guy but he doesn't always look where he is going.

The fattening house has a slurry channel running along its whole length. The end section is in an open area so a tractor can get in and pump it out.

One day, we had taken the metal covers off the access end and Chris walked in thinking about something else and fell straight into three feet of gunge. We pulled him out, unharmed, and brushed the worst off him, but then we had to get him home.

On the basis of 'the buck stops here', I covered the passenger seat of my car with several layers of paper sacks and drove him home with the windows open. I left him on his doorstep to give his own explanations and went home to explain to my family why the car smelt different.

# HOW TO BUY YOUR PIGS

The first thing that you have to decide is the type of pig you want. Not the breed, the type.

Modern pigs have been taken apart and stuck together again and again by geneticists. This is part of the ongoing search to improve the economic qualities in the slaughter pig including growth rate, more lean meat, less fat, meat quality and the ability to respond to high-tech rations.

Pig improvement is highly admirable and has been going on steadily for hundreds of years, but in the last few decades the rate of progress has been extraordinary.

In some modern breeds and hybrid strains a number of qualities have inevitably been weakened, either deliberately because they were not at the time considered important, or by accident. Qualities like flavour and succulence in the meat, docility and the ability to thrive on food that would otherwise be wasted while living in fairly bracing conditions. Even more fundamental qualities have been lost in some strains, such as strong bone structure and well-formed feet. These qualities still persist though among the pigs of a small group of enthusiasts who belong to the Rare Breed Survival Trust. Over the years they have helped the survival of old fashioned breeds which could otherwise have vanished, and by doing so have maintained a valuable gene pool for the future use of geneticists.

*A valuable gene pool*

Commercially though it has often been a struggle as these older breeds generally have more external fat and thus less visual appeal on supermarket shelves. The breeds have endearing and evocative names, with their different qualities and characteristics.

**The Gloucester Old Spot:** Good grazers and clearer-uppers of west country cider orchards, they are very docile, long living and extremely hardy.

**Tamworths:** A lean pig with a deep ginger colour and a long snout ideal for clearing rough ground, and when we do get a hot summer it doesn't get sunburnt. Once renowned for bacon.

**Berkshire:** A black pig with white feet, famed for the delicacy and flavour of the meat and exported in great numbers to Japan.

**Essex and Wessex,** with their distinctive white saddle, also known as **Saddlebacks:** Lovely pigs and once very widespread, though sharing with the Large Black the slight problem of black hair pigment in the belly meat.

**The Large Black:** Totally black as its name suggests and with floppy ears so it is even less likely to try and escape than the others. Is docile and has good mothering abilities.

**The Middle White:** With an amiable squashed up face like a Pekinese, a very attractive beast that also has good mothering abilities.

**The British Lop,** which refers to its ears: A pure white breed again and a good grazer. It originated in the far south west and there are fewer of these around.

Do not go by descriptions though, if you fancy one of these go and have a look for yourself. The best place for an unbiased view is a Rare Breed Centre open to the public.

There is another point to bear in mind and this applies to any breed of any animal. Differences in families and strains within a breed can often be as great as differences between breeds. Also pigs will usually do well if the owner likes the look of them.

All this does not mean in any way that the modern pig is unsuited for life in your half acre, it's just different. It will grow faster and produce a carcass with less fat and more lean meat. It will need higher quality food and with plenty of human contact it should be quiet and docile.

Keepers of Rare Breed pigs including Rare Breed Centres where you may well have more choice, are nearly as rare as their pigs, and you may find it easier to get a pair of pigs from your friendly local pig farmer.

Types of commercial pigs to fatten vary considerably to the experienced eye. Breeding stock in the UK comes mostly from breeding companies, with a small proportion from pedigree breeders. The main traditional breeds in commercial use are Large White with prick ears and Landrace with floppy ears, plus imported Hampshire and Duroc.

The breeding companies use these plus a bewildering selection of hybrids and special lines for special purposes. Many of these are a cocktail from all over the world, bringing in some advantages but often unwanted characteristics as well.

The most useful imports are probably from Europe, particularly Belgium. Here pigs derived from the Belgian Landrace and Pietrain have brought much needed extra muscle and lean meat to the lean (through absence of fat) but less meaty modern British strains. However, all this is just for background. What concerns you is to try, if you are having a commercial pig, to get weaners bred especially for meat from a meat line boar line if you have the choice. A good strain will give you between 2 and 4 per cent more lean meat on the hams and back, which may not sound much but makes a lot of difference to the amount of meat in your freezer.

To summarise your choice then, and sticking carefully to generalities, modern pigs will grow faster, have less fat and more lean meat but will need more expensive food to achieve this. Rare Breed pigs will have more external fat (except the Tamworth) and less lean but this lean may well be more succulent due to minute strands of intramuscular fat. They will generally be more docile and amenable and able to thrive on cheaper food. An ideal compromise would be progeny from a Rare Breed female crossed with a modern meat line boar if you can find it.

Having made your choice, live pigs are usually sold at two stages for fattening on, at 30 kg as weaners, (a misnomer as actual weaning weight is about 7 kg or less), or as feeders at around 45 kg. At 30 kg they should be around 10 to 12 weeks old and this is probably the best size to get, as they are cheaper and more easily handled at this age.

The price may vary considerably from week to week, depending on supply and demand, but also on a whole raft of other factors over which pig farmers have no control. These factors will affect whether they feel more suicidal or slightly more hopeful.

It is therefore worth asking your nearest livestock market to send you a weekly market information sheet so that when you want to buy you have a rough idea of prices and trends.

Apart from the markets, weaners and feeders are sold through livestock groups on contract or by private treaty. Here though they are sold in large groups so to buy your one or two pigs you need to find an amenable pig farmer.

Most pig farmers are helpful, shrewd, very hard working and incorrigible optimists but you also need, in your presumed state of innocence, to know a little about their pigs. The person who knows their pigs best will be their vet.

He (or she), of course, will not give you any information about his clients but if you explain your situation and ask him if he could recommend a pig unit which might sell two or three meaty type weaners of a reasonably healthy standard, he should be able to help.

Not all vets deal with pigs, though, (pets are much more profitable) so you need a vet with a country practice. Even there you may have to search a bit, 'pig vets' are much more thin on the ground in the rainy west for instance where sheep and cattle predominate than in East Anglia or Yorkshire.

To complete the circle, to find this elusive person ring up a couple of pig farmers and ask them who their vet is. An advantage of doing this is that when you have pigs of your own you have already found a suitable vet, in the unlikely event that you need one.

Having found someone who will sell you your pigs, you must expect to pay a little over the market price because you are basically a nuisance to him and he is doing you a favour. You will probably want them delivered, so he will have to get a movement licence and go and select out a couple of half decent pigs from a group.

Make sure, by the way, that you ask for two of the same sex, preferably females, called gilts. Male piglets are no longer castrated, a process which made them grow more slowly and put on fat. The practice was a relic of the times when pigs grew very slowly and were sold well after puberty and developed boar taint if left entire. Males in general will grow faster, eat more and be leaner but they do get pretty precocious at three to four months, hence same sex pigs.

You should hope to get bright eyed shiny coated pigs without too big a stomach. It's always possible he might sell you a couple of older slower growing pigs that have had a check and been put back a class. It might help to ask to see the group they are coming from, though if he says 'no' it's not because he has something to hide but probably because he doesn't let anyone in, so as to keep out disease.

If he will tolerate you on the unit, dressed in his overalls and boots, spend as long as you can, in fact keep going back, just to watch and study the pigs. At first you will be an object of extreme interest to them but just stay still and quiet, watch them and learn.

Watch their social behaviour; which ones get pushed about and why, which are the top dogs, and their extraordinary behaviour when startled. In the

*Obvious coughs or sneezes...*

process you will start to learn what a healthy pig looks like and which are not doing so well - quite valuable knowledge.

Finally, if you are dealing with a pig unit quite near you bear in mind the owner would far rather you were rearing his pigs than unknowns from elsewhere, which could bring him trouble in the form of disease if they got out.

If you hanker after a couple of Rare Breed pigs, write to the Trust and they will send you a list of breeders. Ask them also for your nearest Rare Breed Centre where you can probably see several breeds together and find out which appeals to you and get ideas on feeding and management.

It's worth mentioning here that the Trust do run an occasional workshop, usually no more than one a year. It is advertised in the quarterly magazine or you can phone and enquire.

Another minor bonus for the older breeds is that if they get out they are more likely to move towards you than depart at high speed for pastures new.

Basically then, buy pigs you like the look of with no obvious coughs and sneezes and you can always get more selective next time round.

In the search for genetic perfection it became desirable to import some boar semen from Belgium, from animals with a very high percentage of lean meat. They also have a tendency to drop down dead if stressed but we got round that one by mating them with very tranquil females.

We could have avoided a maze of health regulations by bringing it in illegally in thermos flasks but we did it all correctly and eventually our share was waiting for us at a university in Kent.

I drove down to fetch it and took delivery of quite a large container hissing with liquid nitrogen with a lid on it.

It was only after I reached home that it occurred to me that had I been involved in any sort of road accident my feet would have gone brittle in about thirty seconds.

# MOVING AND HANDLING

Wild pigs have evolved to be able to crash through thorn thicket and undergrowth, dig up roots and other succulents and live warily in fiercely protective family groups. To maintain this lifestyle they have armour plated shoulders, a very solid head and a tough, pliable and very sensitive nose. They also have a fair turn of speed and manoeuvrability to escape or attack, combined in the boars with ferocious aggression and long sharp curved tusks to disembowel anything within reach.

Before you decide to give up the whole idea of keeping pigs, your 30 kg pigs are many genes and generations from this prototype, though some mellowed, vestigial traces remain. They still have tough shoulders and an enquiring and sensitive snout and they can still move quickly to satisfy an abiding curiosity to find out what lies beyond whatever gates and enclosures you surround them with.

You may at some time decide that you are going to grab an errant pig and march it home. Unlike sheep there is not much to get hold of on a pig, apart from the ears and tail. If you're fit this is fine when they are small, but as they get bigger they get stronger and more energetic and then it gets hard work. They also have four sharp feet which serve as anchors and they make a lot of outraged noise when seized. Though it's surprising what you can do with a burst of adrenalin it won't do your back much good.

The best ways then to move them from A to B are by driving, bribery or a combination of the two. The only times you are likely to have to move pigs is on delivery, when they depart or if they get out.

On the first two, if you cannot get the trailer right up to the pen, you need to give yourself a bit of help by lining the route with hurdles, corrugated iron or whatever, preferably opaque. Even if you only have enough bits and pieces to line one side of the intended route, that's a great help. What is definitely not a help is if a gust of wind blows it all down with a crash half way, so make sure it's all secure.

Time spent in preparation is never wasted. It may seem obvious but if you have a boundary fence round your garden or acres do make sure any gates are shut and any holes plugged. This is a good general rule, not just when you're moving pigs.

Noisy helpful dogs should be kept well away, but small children who love to help can be useful to fill gaps as long as they stand still and quiet.

Another generality is that smaller pigs are easier to drive if you have the time, a combination of curiosity and nervousness making their progress slower. Being closer to the ground they can't see so far ahead so they don't usually try and rush off into the middle distance. This is a generality though; be prepared for the individual.

As a final preparation, to drive pigs you need one essential tool, a pig board. Simple enough to make, you need a two-feet square

*One essential tool, a pig board*

of three-eighths thick exterior plywood, rounded off at the bottom two corners with a hole for a handle in the top side. Now make two more; it's much easier to drive pigs with two people and a spare is always handy.

A surprising number of pig farmers make do with rusty old lengths of corrugated iron which are sometimes okay but not if you need to move fast in a high wind.

Pigs as they grow develop speed and the ability to feint and swerve like a rugby three-quarter when they feel the need, so the first thing to remember when you set about moving larger pigs is to keep the general noise level down. Having been treated in a civilised fashion they will be naturally docile, so talk to them in a quiet friendly voice and no shouting of the 'hey, hey, hey' variety beloved of older pig people or they begin to suspect your intentions.

A gentle hectoring tone lets them know you're still there and have not given up. Another advantage of the gentle touch is that they have no excuse to pretend to be startled and rush about.

As discussed, pigs are good at penetrating hedges, so they don't see sticks or pairs of legs as a problem. You will need something solid and opaque to block their vision. Even a paper sack is quite effective unless one calls your bluff, and, to repeat, the pig board is ideal.

When you first start driving pigs you will probably over react and so will the pig, and you will all get breathless. Soon, however, you will learn to make the minimum signals necessary, and will learn when to stand absolutely still, such as when the pig is going through the gate you want it to.

Again, when you start, there will be times when, however quick you think you are, your reactions will be too slow, but you will soon learn to anticipate their next move. One factor on your side is that although pigs are fast they haven't great stamina for long distance running.

It has been said by aged pig keepers that it takes about twenty years to really get to grips with driving pigs and by then you can't run anyway.

After all these dire warnings the actual driving will probably be a distinct anti-climax. There is though one thing you should be prepared for with larger pigs and that can best be described as the 'woof woof and away syndrome'. Having been penned up for some time, when you open the gate to drive them there will sometimes come a moment, probably in the first thirty seconds when they suddenly realise they can have a real gallop in a straight line and they will bark with joy and off they'll go.

*'Woof woof and away syndrome'*

It usually only lasts for 20 to 30 yards but be prepared, perhaps station a driver at the estimated point of arrival? If they happen to go the right way, all the better. They will stop when they run out of breath, usually with a four wheel skid to avoid crashing into an obstacle.

Two people can drive twenty pigs but it's still a good idea to have two, even with a couple of pigs. As a belt and braces measure, once they associate a rattling bucket with food, one driver can do a Pied Piper act and lay a trail for them to follow. Don't be too lavish though or you will be there all day, and always keep your pig board handy; they could get distracted.

The rules for straight driving are simple. If you have no guiding hurdles, then you take station on each quarter, that is slightly behind and to each side. If you want them to go left the person on the right moves up a bit and vice versa, like a sheep-dog. If you want them to go in a gate or anywhere that causes them to hesitate a bit, don't crowd them, and chat to them gently. Only when they are well through, past the point of no return, do you move in fast.

If you have hurdles on one side, one driver stays at the rear, the other walks on the unprotected side. He or she can then slip ahead if need be, to open a gate or whatever.

If they turn and want to go back, bring your pig board firmly up to their nose and if they push, put your foot behind it. Make sure though that you are able to move it quickly in case the pig tries to swerve round. It's really just commonsense and will all come naturally to you once you start.

If your plan is to drive them onto a trailer or lorry, prepare that with equal care. Make the ramp as shallow as possible using any sloping ground you may have and if you can, park the vehicle alongside a wall so one side is secure.

Straw the ramp well and if you can make the sides solid so the pigs can't see through, this will help. Pigs appear to have no head for heights and although you know that they can't fall through a six inch gap, they don't share this knowledge. Finally put hurdles in a V shape to funnel them onto the ramp.

When they step on to the ramp they will probably stop. Don't let them; this is the one time you need to give them swift and vigorous encouragement to keep on going. If they turn and start coming down again it gets a lot harder.

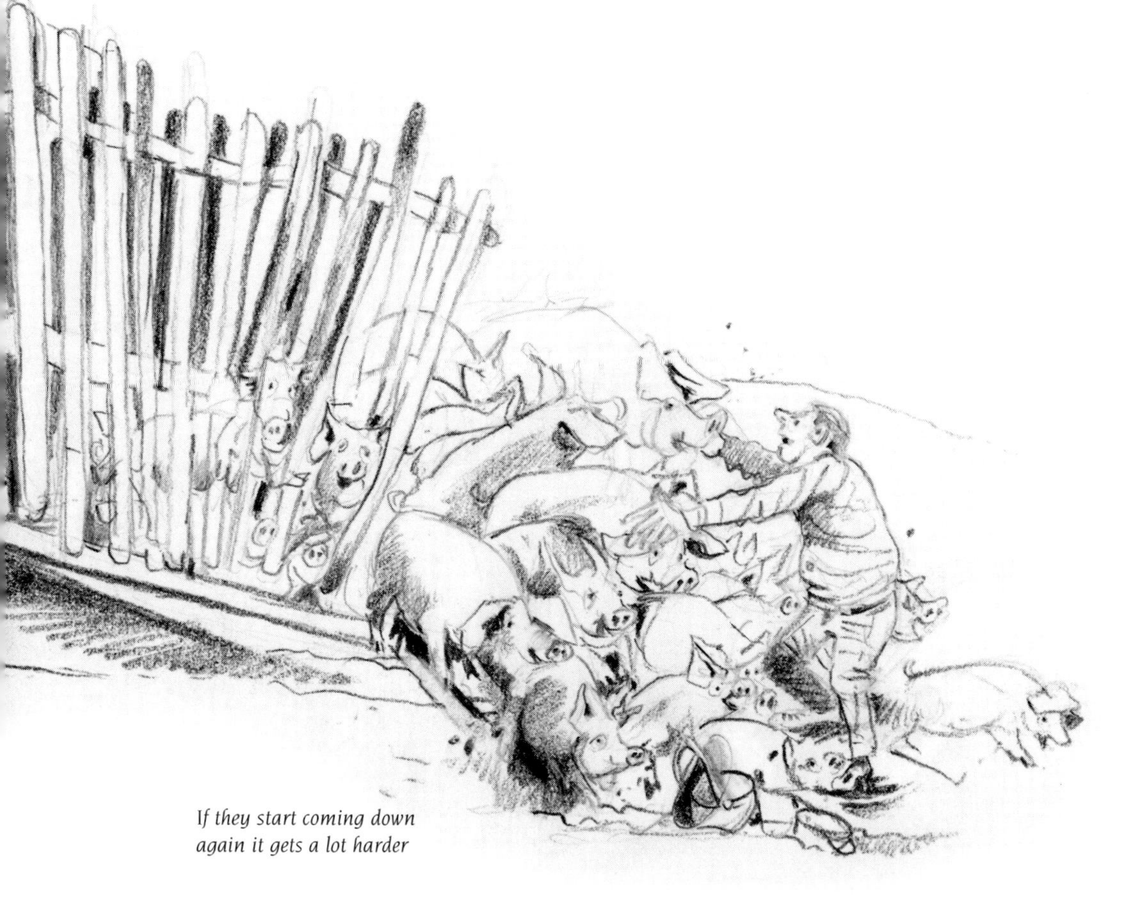

*If they start coming down again it gets a lot harder*

The other time when you might have to do a bit of driving is if the pigs get out. The chief causes for this are leaving a gate unlatched, something breaking or the pigs getting under, over or through a barrier.

If you need help to get them back, buy yourself some time by throwing something tasty in front of them that will keep them in one place. It is about this time that you wish you'd always put the pig boards in one place so you can find them in a hurry.

If your pigs escape from an electric fenced enclosure never take up the wire and try to drive them through the gap. Having good memories they won't go through where the wire was on any account. Put them back through the non-electrified gate or hurdle entrance.

You may not have time to erect a lot of hurdles, maybe you haven't got a lot of hurdles, but remember to put one up to funnel them back into their pen. If you can only get one back at a time, have some food handy so you can keep the first one occupied while you are getting the next one through the gate. If they go outside your property they won't go far.

Finally, when you find them wandering, don't panic and wave your arms about, as this will only make them want to go somewhere further and quieter.

The ancient and probably Saxon collective noun for pigs was a 'dryft' of swine, which is as evocative as you can get.

*Don't panic and wave your arms about*

We were showing young breeding stock to a group of overseas customers and it was suggested that they would like to see some of the adult sires.

Moving adult boars about near other stock is tricky so we took precautions. Three of us with pig boards got the boar in question and walked him up and down, watching him like a hawk. It should be explained that a few years with pigs sharpen up your reactions to a high degree.

As I went to edge him round holding my pig board between us he was showing signs of irritability. Suddenly he gave a sideways uppercut lunge at me which I parried with the board. It didn't quite work, though, because he continued the flick up and neatly scored a deep groove in the palm of my exposed hand where I gripped the board. Without the pig board he would have scored a much deeper groove up my thigh.

The visiting breeders decided that perhaps they didn't want that particular blood line but the boar's tusk does make an excellent letter opener.

# FEEDING

Pigs in the wild are foragers, consumers of an infinite variety of leaves, roots, seeds, fruits and the odd small dead animal. Their abilities and qualities cannot be put better than in this quotation from a book of 1733:

> These creatures, though in many respects disagreeable, are of considerable importance to the community at large and to farmers in particular; this race of animals whose stomachs seem a receptacle for everything which other creatures refuse, and which, but for these, would be entirely wasted. They industriously gather up and greedily devour what would otherwise be trodden underfoot and wasted. The refuse of the fields, the gardens, the barns, and the scullery, to them is a feast.

Since distant times when pigs were first domesticated, herds were allowed to continue this economical diet, in temperate climates finishing the year in oak forests clearing the acorns. In the autumn before food became really scarce, most of them were slaughtered and salted down for the winter.

*They will eat nearly anything*

Pigs are omnivores; they will eat nearly anything and turn most things into succulent pork. As in most of life though you get out what you put in and a diet of rubbish won't produce the best meat. On the other hand what you may consider rubbish the pig may consider five star nosh, so it's useful to understand the pig's dietary needs.

The pig is not a ruminant so its digestive system can't use large amounts of vegetation and fibre. In fact it has a digestive system very similar to humans. The traditional way of feeding pigs, for the last few hundred years anyway, has been a mixture of grains - wheat, barley and middlings, plus protein, usually milk or skim milk when in surplus, and in this century fish meal and soya. Middlings, by the way, is the valuable nutritious outer part of the wheat grain taken away before the rest is made into white bread for humans.

Although pigs in the wild are constant rooters and nibblers, the domesticated pig, for reasons of convenience, has traditionally been fed twice a day with the meals as widely spaced as possible. This doesn't mean that if you feel like throwing in something succulent that is to hand you have to wait. In fact, it's a good idea to break the feeding routine a bit. The pig's time clock is not accurate to half an hour or so and they sometimes noisily demand food well before the due time.

Modern pigs are grown very fast on fairly high-tech diets, computers being used to select the cheapest ingredients to achieve the required specification. With the big feed suppliers this can include grains, seeds and proteins including

*Breaking the feeding routine*

some very unusual things from all over the world, plus the essential minerals, vitamins and trace elements. It may also have natural gut flora modifiers to stimulate growth and antibiotics to ward off disease.

Pig rations start about the same price as gold dust, weight for weight but are generally cost effective, and get less expensive as the pig grows. The downside is that it then eats more.

The first ration is called a creep ration; sweet and tasty to encourage the inquisitive piglet to start eating, and to help it adapt its intestines to digest carbohydrate. Creep comes from the name of the warm sheltered area where the piglets sleep, warmer than their mother wants to be and protected from being flattened by her one hundred times bigger bulk.

The second is the weaner ration, fed from soon after weaning at 6 to 7 kilos and around four weeks old up to around 12 to 15 kilos.

The rest are grower and finisher rations decreasing in expensive protein and slightly increasing in fibre as the pig grows older and bigger.

A high proportion of pigs in this country are killed at a fairly low weight, and therefore a young age, dictated to a certain extent by supermarket pressure. The resulting meat is bland in taste with little fat and sometimes a bit dry when cooked. Pigs can't be exported at this light weight because on the continent they like them bigger, older and tastier.

Generally, and you can't be too dogmatic about anything to do with pigs, the larger they are when they are killed and the slower they grow, the better the flavour.

On the other hand there are trials where the results showed that pigs grown fast on an ad-lib diet produced more acceptable meat, though it didn't say to whom it was more acceptable. You pays your money and takes your choice - it depends what you are used to.

By using a more adaptable 'old-fashioned' animal with a much more varied diet and slower growth, you should be edging towards the quality and flavour of meat from the wild.

Except, and there is usually an 'except', to get this leaner, more healthy and more flavoursome carcass, for we too are what we eat, you must grow pigs on a high quality diet when they are young. A basic rule is that the smaller the pig and the smaller its stomach, the more nutritious and thus expensive its diet. This largesse will ensure the growth of a good bone and muscle structure which will stand it in good stead during the rest of its growth period. If it has been fed a cheaper adult ration too young it will be pot bellied and tend to lay on more fat than normal.

Growing pigs is a compromise between various factors; cost and quality of food, growth rate, effect of buildings, genetics and weight at slaughter. The factors go on and on, but feed cost weighs heavily, making up about 71 per cent of the total cost of keeping pigs professionally, depending how clever you are at it.

Doing it your way on your scale, food can be cheap or free and the profit imperative is low, so you can go for quality pork in the sense of slower growth and varied diet without financial pain.

To resume, having got the pigs growing well for the first few weeks you can start experimenting with whatever you can find from the vast variety of 'waste' foods available. As long as you feed a balancer ration of 1 to 2 kilos a day of meal or cubes and make the rest of the diet as varied as possible, you won't go far wrong. A bit like humans again - in the wild, pigs given the availability will balance their diet themselves. In your pig pen they depend on you.

When you first get your pigs you may find they will turn their noses up at your tentatively offered green-stuff, but this is nothing personal. If this is the first time they have ever seen any it may take a day or so to get a taste for something new and strange.

Do not, please, overdo the green approach, especially when they are young. To repeat, they haven't got cows' stomachs and digestive systems and the ability to deal with huge amounts of fibre and cellulose. You could easily give them diarrhoea, affectionately known in the trade as the scours (see chapter 5).

The best way of getting your meal or cubes is from the farmer you bought your pigs from, though just check what additives against disease he is adding to feed, and buy it by volume to avoid any clash with regulations.

You can then share some of the cost benefits of bulk buying, though he will probably charge you for the hassle of having to bag it up from a bulk bin. An extra advantage is that the pigs will continue on the same food that they are used to.

Any sudden change, be it food, environment or even human keeper, can create some stress, usually showing up as a check in growth rate. It won't affect your pigs very much, as they are incredibly durable and hardy, but it's worth being aware of it.

*See they get equal shares*

Now let's deal with your actual feeding. The basic things to remember here are common to all livestock feeding.

First make sure that the food is clean when eaten, that is, that it hasn't been mixed with urine or faeces. Female pigs pee backwards and don't study where they are pointing. They may well still eat the revolting mix but with less enthusiasm or benefit.

Secondly see that they get equal shares. There will usually be one pig (the boss) who will try and get more than his share, or one may be a slower eater.

This action of the boss pig is not because it is greedy, unkind and selfish - you mustn't give them human values. This is the inherited gene for the survival of the fittest. The only time this is reversed is when a mother pig will give up food for its young, the survival of the species.

If you have two or three pigs, have a trough each, free-standing or fixed (see the chapter on housing), and put them at opposite corners of the pen. Boss pig will decide his mate has nicer food and shoulder him out of the way, but number two can then nip smartly over to boss pig's trough just as quickly.

Alternatively use the bed as a trough, for dry food only though. Anything that makes the bed wet or even damp is bad news. If you spread the food wide and evenly on the bed you have a large 'trough' area. Both or all get a chance to get their share and the bed is kept in a dry and salubrious state.

Feeding on a bed with a false roof over it is a little more difficult in cold weather, so you will have to decide whether it's worth the effort.

If you have your pigs in an outside run and you are feeding your meal part of the ration as cubes, there is no problem throwing them on the ground, provided the ground is dry. If it's at all boggy, or you want to feed wet meal, use a light metal or plastic round trough, even a washing up bowl will do.

Put the two or three troughs wide apart and they will get even shares. The easiest way is to fill the troughs first and plonk them over the wire. If you try to fill them in the enclosure the pigs will usually tip the trough up as you pour and they will fight over one trough.

Clean available water is of prime importance. They must have a supply on top of any water they get in wet mash. Water in a free-standing trough will very quickly be tipped over, or they will push in rubbish, blow bubbles and walk in it, and eventually pee in it.

If you use a large rectangular cattle trough in a fenced run, fix enough bars across so they can't bathe in it. Also make sure that any tank or waterer has a non-return valve between it and the mains. A final word on tanks - check it regularly for slime and dead birds and make it big enough to support maximum flow rates.

The waterer can either be a small bowl type with a ballcock protected by a flap, or a nipple drinker which they learn to bite. Height is more important with nipple drinkers. You may need one low one for when they are small and

*...so they can't bathe in it*

a higher one for later. A variable height adjustable drinker is by far the best alternative. The pig's head and neck should slope upwards at 15 degrees when drinking from a nipple drinker, and this alone will cut waste of water by some 40 per cent. Ask around for a type that doesn't fall apart, has easy access for cleaning and tries not to leak. Well engineered and simple in fact. Whatever you do there will be some spillage so put it near the bottom of a slope.

Warm food especially in winter saves the pig using up energy to heat it to body temperature, so it grows better and saves you money. Tastier too.

The older and more robust self-sufficiency books extol the virtues of the pig bucket, into which went all the plate scrapings and the first greasy rinse off the washing up. This is now illegal.

Feeding green-stuff on the outside pen floor can mean a lot of waste and extra barrow loads at cleaning out time, as any not eaten at once will become inedible fairly quickly. You could chop it up and feed it in the trough or contrive a wire or metal rack to hang over the side of the pen wall.

Little four-legged beasties will rapidly come and set up home if you provide them with free available food. Store any meal or cubes in a safe container; a dustbin with a good fitting lid is fine, and clear up any spillage. Popular times for rats and mice to arrive are in the spring when they start to breed and in the autumn when they come in from the hedges and arable fields. In a mild winter they may keep on breeding.

Keep some rat/mice poison down permanently in a sheltered place, under a piece of propped up slate or similar and renew it if it looks stale or vanishes. Make sure the cover is pet and bird safe. A good hunting cat is also highly effective, one with yellow eyes and ragged ears is ideal.

Free food can be anything from the vegetable garden or the kitchen as long as you remember the proviso about feeding kitchen waste. It is probably best to avoid vegetation from flowers unless you are sure it is safe, as a lot of flowers and shrubs are poisonous. As long as you steer clear of deadly nightshade, hemlock, yew, bracken and the more lurid fungi, wild green-stuff is fairly safe.

Apart from grass it can include matured acorns, sloes, small branches and their leaves, windfall apples, weeds from your vegetable garden, try anything. The more variety in the diet, the tastier the meat. One gentle warning - don't forget that hemlock at first glance looks like cow parsley, only darker green and with a smooth blotchy stem.

Should you be fortunate enough to live in a cheese making county you might have a source of skim milk or whey, wonderful food if you can get it, a protein supplement that makes pigs blossom, but see the chapter on regulations first.

*Straw is not strictly food*

Regarding the local baker and all his stale bread and cakes, this would make your pigs contented. However under lunatic EU laws you need to become a registered animal charity before this is allowed. Under this Directive, waste cakes and bread can only be transported by someone other than the baker if they have a waste carrier's permit costing over £100 from the Environment Agency. It doesn't finish there though. It has to go to someone who is licensed to receive waste, (the permit costs a second mortgage), and then it must be buried in a tip. In Europe if they have heard of it they laugh hysterically and sensibly ignore it.

Straw is not strictly food, though you will find they eat a lot of it. You will need about ten to twelve small bales for two pigs for the time they are with you, depending on how cold it is and how clean you and they keep the beds.

The bales must be kept dry and preferably stacked so a cat can get between them. If you have to keep them outdoors keep them off the ground and cover with plastic or similar. The best straw for bedding is wheat straw and after a good sunny harvest it should be bright yellow, shiny and difficult to break. If it's grey and brittle it's either old or been lying in the wet, or both.

A rough guide to feeding rates for meal or cubes:

30 to 40 kg wt. 12-13 weeks old, 1.5 kg per day of a good grower ration

40 to 70 kg wt. 15-16 weeks old plus, 2-2.5 kg per day plus an increasing proportion of waste foods

The biggest variable here is the type of pig you have and the feeding value of any waste food. This advice is roughly right for a modern hybrid pig, but if you have rare breed traditional stock then the type of food can be altered and made cheaper. Firstly they will not need a high-tech ration; wheat and barley meal plus a vitamin and mineral supplement and 5 to 10 per cent soya meal will be fine.

The best way to find out how much to feed them is by trial and error. Give them as much as they will clear up in ten minutes twice a day, or three times when they are young. Next day you'll know how much to feed, and you will need to gradually increase it as they grow older, depending how much nourishing waste food you have.

In the last month cut back to around four pounds per day and give extra green-stuff, because it's at this stage that these older breeds can start to put on fat. It isn't an exact science so get advice with your first ones if you think they are getting too fat or too thin and hungry. If they are bouncy, shiny coated, bright eyed and nicely meaty then you have probably got it about right.

The fattening houses are fed by an automatic pipeline system with each pen fed a measured quantity of nourishing porridge.

At thankfully fairly rare occasions the pipe blocks.

The pen before the blockage noisily gobbling down its breakfast goes relatively quiet. The pigs in the pen after the blockage, suddenly deprived and driven mad by the sight and sound of their neighbours' noisy enjoyment, take their protest to around 150 decibels.

The rest of the several hundred unfed pigs, awakened by the sound of the feed system starting up, very quickly reach the same ear splitting level.

The also unfed duty pig staff, in a maelstrom of noise and agitated swine, have to start undoing the pipeline with huge stilsons and get deluged with porridge and water. Communication is by sign language, often explicit.

Finally, it gets fixed and relative peace is restored. We resolve to make sure we know where the spanners are for next time and, wet and soggy, return to our breakfast.

# HEALTH, DISEASE AND VETS

The more pigs you have in one place, the more careful you have to be with disease prevention and promoting health. Fortunately the converse is also true, so with your two or three the problems should be minimal. It is summed up by the maxim that the worst enemy of a pig is another pig.

Another thing in your favour is that pigs, like most living things, are at their most vulnerable when they are very young, and by the time they start the fattening stage when you take delivery there should be very little trouble.

The above contains generalisations that would not even be whispered by a professional pig farmer, but you get the idea. Pigs are also incredibly tough and durable, unlike sheep which tend to drop dead if you take your eyes off them for more than ten minutes; it takes a lot to kill a pig.

The best way to know if a pig needs attention is to know what a healthy one looks like. To get to the stage where this is second nature you need to work with pigs for some time until any abnormality stands out immediately like a sore thumb, even in a large group of pigs. How long this takes varies with the person and some people never get there, so there follows a simple checklist of areas of disease.

*The first symptom of an ill pig is that it won't eat*

Although it's a gross over-simplification there are three major areas of problems in pigs, each with a number of different causes:

1. Lameness, which is generally an injured or infected foot, a leg joint or a hurt back
2. Intestinal, usually evidenced by diarrhoea or the scours, or less often constipation
3. Respiratory, coughing, sneezing, eyes running or a twisted nose.

The first major symptom if a pig is ill is that it won't eat. There may be a simple explanation, like it has over eaten or a mate has piddled in its trough. If its mate though is clamouring for food and the other is lying down all broody then it's probably ill.

The next step is to take its temperature. A veterinary thermometer is a vital tool that you must have, in fact always keep a second as a spare. A healthy pig's temperature is 101.5 to 103.5 degrees F. Below these limits often indicates something more serious than a high temperature, but in either case talk to your vet.

Taking the temperature is simple. Shake the thermometer down first, hold the pig's tail with one hand to keep control and contact and insert the thermometer carefully in the anus, holding it sideways against the anal wall. Keep it there for about 30 seconds. If you are not skilled in reading a thermometer, it might be a good idea to have a practice first before you meet an ill pig.

Also, shut the pig in the outside run before you start or it will walk you inside on your hands and knees. Your pig may of course not have much tail to grab

*Not much tail to grab hold of*

hold of; it's often half cut off at birth to stop tail biting, a vice of closely confined pigs. This can make life more difficult, though if it's ill it probably won't be feeling very frisky.

Right, so you have established that something is wrong. The next thing is to be able to give the vet a summary of any other symptoms when you ring. This will help him to judge whether he needs to roar off now crashing red lights on the way, or it can wait until it fits in with his other visits.

Check on the following points:

1. Can it get up by itself and if it walks does it limp or show signs of pain?
2. Is breathing laboured or very fast? (Is it breathing?!)
3. Is it coughing or sneezing or making other odd noises?
4. Have its eyes been running, leaving dark brown stains down from the corners?
5. Has it turned an odd colour anywhere, like red or purple blotches, or have its ears gone blue?
6. Is it scouring or constipated? The first will be very evident, the latter shown by a scattering of hard little musket balls. Check and see if its stomach is hard and swollen.
7. Finally is it acting oddly in any other way, like walking round in circles or banging its head against the wall?

To summarise, when you ring your vet tell him first the size or age of your pigs and where you got them from. Then the symptoms including the temperature, even if it's normal, and how long since you noticed anything. These checks should cover most of the ills that pigs are prone to, but don't have nightmares, pigs on a small scale are usually pretty healthy.

If you are worried though don't delay hoping the problem will get better tomorrow. Generally the longer you delay the more chance there is that the condition will become chronic and the more it will cost before it's well again.

A word about vets. Veterinary science like everything else has become more complex and necessarily more specialised. It follows, for example, that if you live around Newmarket many of the vets will be expert on horses while in town centres veterinary hospitals will deal mainly with pets in the form of small animals. Similarly in Wales the vets will be highly skilled with sheep and cattle.

Although it is not so vital in your case as with a professional pig farmer, if you can, use a 'pig vet' who deals with pigs all the time. Perhaps talk to the chap who supplied your pigs for advice.

A final point to think of before you lift the phone is that vets are professional people with a lot of overheads and it will cost you a second mortgage before they get out of their car. You also have to decide whether your pigs are pets or meat on the hoof.

People tend to spend on pets whatever is needed and prices reflect this, but with a pig to fill your freezer there is no point in running up a vast bill on an animal worth only a fraction of it. The moral is don't rush to ring your vet for trivial things, and if in doubt why not first ring your friendly local pig farmer. Perhaps you could barter any skills you have for his occasional advice and help.

A list of pig diseases would go twice round the equator but if you avoid buying in anything which is lame, coughing, sneezing or scouring you have cut out most of them. Remember too that unlike a pig breeder who is stuck with whatever bugs he has, you de-populate every three months or so and, after a cleanout and a short rest, can start again with a clean slate.

One problem that you can do something about yourself is mange. Mange in pigs is caused by a mite that burrows under the skin producing itching and irritation and in bad cases brown encrustation. Most pigs have the mite but in a healthy growing pig it's not evident and causes no apparent harm. If your pig keeps rubbing and scratching itself against hard edges there are several possible treatments.

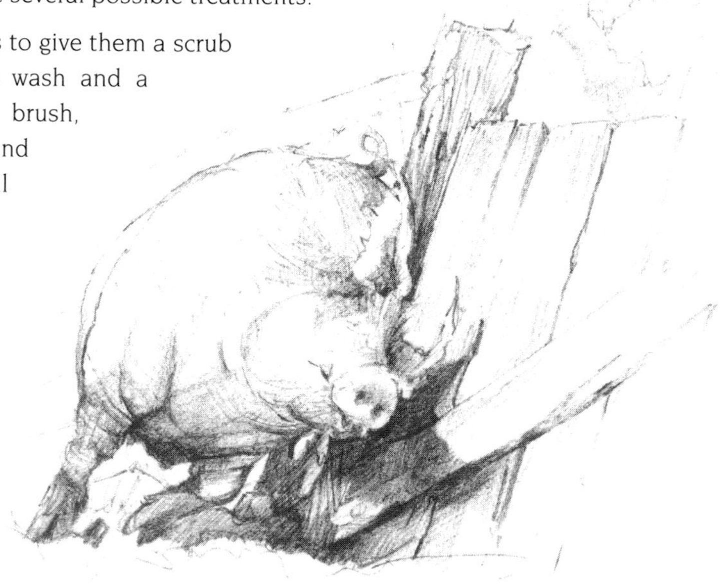

The simplest is to give them a scrub with a mange wash and a medium stiff brush, especially around the ears, tail and mid back. They will protest loudly when small so pen them in a small area. If you really want to give them a treat, periodically pour some paraffin oil, known as pig oil, down their backs or put in a post at 45 degrees with a bit of oily sacking nailed to it as a rubbing post. If you have used a mange wash they will need washing again after three weeks, to kill any newly hatched mites and there will still be eggs around the pen in woodwork.

However it's unusual to see mange in fit, fast growing animals and once cleaned they are not usually worried by the mites. To get rid of them completely a three week gap between batches will kill the little devils by starvation and, in case you're worried, they don't affect humans.

Also when you buy your pigs check whether they have been wormed and when they will need doing again.

Any medicines, unless on veterinary prescription, can usually be got from travelling salesmen, most areas have one, who also carry a range of equipment. You can't impulse buy though, as regulations state that he must have the order from you before he calls.

There are other diseases that might come up in conversation and it's handy to have heard of them.

Firstly are chronic afflictions like enzootic pneumonia and rhinitis, various forms of enteritis, dysentery and meningitis. It would also be worth asking your supplier of pigs if they need to be vaccination against erysipelas. Then there are the notifiable diseases like foot and mouth, swine fever and Aujesky's disease where herds are slaughtered by the Ministry and part compensation paid.

In another category are the latest imported virus diseases like pig flu and the dreaded blue ear, and new ones appear regularly. Blue ear has spread to a majority of herds and it lowers the immunity to disease of a whole herd, so problems up to then under control start causing havoc. It appears to go away after a period but can recur. There are at least two more complex virus afflictions. As has been stressed before none of these is likely to affect you very much, but awareness of them is useful in conversation with pig people.

To repeat, the main thing you need to achieve, and there is no desperate hurry, it will come in due course, is the ability to recognise when your pigs are sick.

Finally, on disease prevention it is useful again to remember that the chief enemy of a pig is another pig and after that people who have been near them. If you go wandering round livestock markets or near other people's pigs don't track bugs back to yours on your boots.

If you want to do the job properly, keep a spare pair of large wellies and overalls for piggy visitors including the vet. If you decide to make them dip their feet in disinfectant, make it up fresh each time but do make sure the wellies are leak-proof; nothing evaporates the enthusiasm for health precautions as fast as a soggy disinfected foot.

The grain to feed the pigs is stored in a metal silo some thirty feet high and which sits on an insulated base of bitumen.

To check the grain is not overheating it is necessary to climb up a metal ladder to the side of the silo and shove a thermometer at the end of a ten foot metal rod down into the grain. A simple job.

One day, I collected the metal thermometer and leant it against the side of the silo, climbed halfway up the ladder and grabbed the metal pole preparatory to climbing up the rest of the way to the top.

As I grabbed it the rod was still touching the ground. What I didn't know but which became immediately apparent was there was an electric short in the auger feeding the silo and that the whole thing was live.

I was now part of the connection between the live silo and the earth, round the back of the silo and out of sight.

It was a happy ending, my convulsions took the rod off the ground, breaking the circuit. I threw the rod down and very cautiously and gratefully climbed back down to earth. Farms are dangerous places.

# HUSBANDRY AND STRESS

Husbandry is a magic word. The quality of good husbandry is inherent in those fortunate people who are 'good with animals'. Some people are born with it, some need practice to acquire it and to some it will always be a closed book. Interestingly, people who have green fingers with machinery are often indifferent husbandry-men, and the converse is often destructively true.

Good husbandry in its simplest form could be described as the ability to put yourself mentally in the animal's place, of having a sympathetic understanding of how it feels. This is a necessary foundation on which to build experience.

One of the aims of good husbandry is to reduce undue stress, which is just as destructive with pigs as it is with humans.

By the time you take charge of your 30 kg pigs they will already have been through several major stress points, some natural and others not natural but necessary. Having 10 to 12 brothers and sisters born at the same time and fighting for a good teat and the life preserving colostrum (which is only there for a few hours), is a tough start.

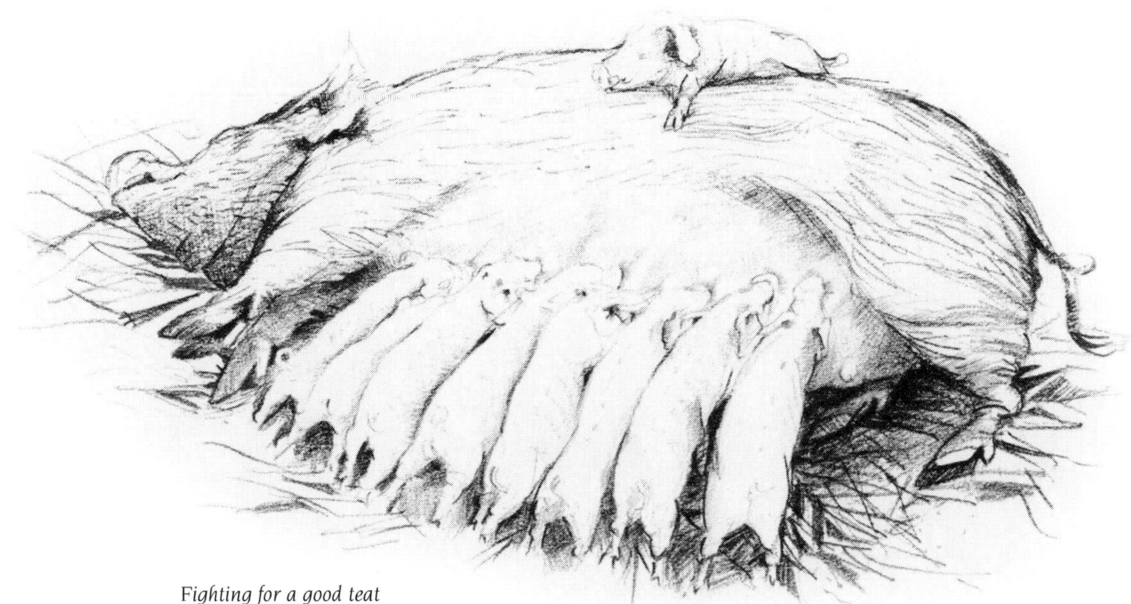

*Fighting for a good teat*

The piglets will then have their long eye teeth clipped, to prevent them ripping up their siblings faces in the struggle for milk. In the wild where nature takes its course the weaker and any damaged pigs would die.

They will also be treated with an iron solution, usually by injection, to hold off anaemia until they can start on solid food. In the wild they would root in fresh earth and get their iron from that.

From birth onwards some may get scours, or diarrhoea, and be treated with whatever works on that farm. If it's not treated quickly this may damage their gut lining and their ability from then on to grow as fast as their peers.

At around 3 to 4 weeks of age and weighing 6 to 7 kilos they will have their biggest stress point when they are weaned. Suddenly their source of security, warmth and food vanishes, although everything is done to cushion this, with extra warmth and special food. In the wild weaning is later; when they are big enough to forage for themselves, the sow's milk dries up and she starts to think about the next generation.

Shortly after this 3 to 4 week weaning they have another stress point where they are mixed in groups for size, and finally after a few more weeks your two pigs are selected out, meet wheeled transport for the first time and are delivered to your tender mercies.

From this you will see the point of letting them settle in quietly for a couple of days while they get accustomed to fresh surroundings, noises, food and faces. You can help a bit here by keeping them for a while on the same food as they are used to.

In a few days however they will be relishing the absence of competition, the extra space and one to one attention. As a general rule, the smaller the pig the more changes affect it, and it is always good husbandry to try and make any changes gradually. Don't worry about it unduly though; at the most, even a sudden change will only affect the growth rate for a few days.

Stress relief of course works two ways. As P. G. Wodehouse fans know there are few things more relaxing and civilized than chatting to pigs over a wall.

Heat stress can affect pigs badly. You can just wear fewer clothes if it's hot; the pig is encased in a layer of fat and has no sweat glands. Pigs when uncomfortably hot will pant and get irritable and restless. Make sure they have shade if they are outside. The only way they can lose heat is by conduction with something cooler, a mud wallow being ideal. If they are in an outside grass enclosure just run a hose into a dip in the ground, or dig a hole. A mud wallow also helps with sunburn if you have white pigs.

*She starts thinking about the next generation*

A *mud wallow is ideal*

The need for a cool wallow has gained pigs a deeply entrenched reputation for being dirty, for if there is no mud they will naturally roll in whatever is available.

Coming loosely under the term of husbandry, pigs like to be rubbed where they can't reach, like down the centre of their backs and in the little dip beside the eye and, when they are a little older and get to know you, a stomach rub will get them to lie down or at least stand still. George Henderson in his book *Farmer's Progress* says that if you really want to make friends with a pig, tickle the roof of its mouth; it has a hypnotic effect and you can do anything with it. Watch your fingers though.

Pigs have a high intelligence, get easily bored and suffer from chronic curiosity. In the wild they get plenty of stimulation - see how they react when they get startled - but cooped up they do get bored. Their affliction of chronic curiosity leads them to investigate and eat or destroy anything if given the chance, like the buttons of a coat left carelessly over a wall.

As in most species pigs establish a pecking order, deciding which one is boss and, in a larger group, which one makes the tea. As mentioned in the chapter on feeding, make sure number two gets its fair share of food and warm bedding.

A *watchful glance at your torch...*

Cold weather is a good time to check if you are mentally putting yourself in the pigs' place. Just because you are warm from exercise or whatever and the sun is shining, don't presume the pigs are too. They may not be able to get out of a piercing draught and they can't just go and get an anorak.

Remember it is at night when it is usually coldest and it's also the longest period when you won't see them. It is good practice to make a point of checking they have warm bedding at dusk, probably to be met by a sleepy enquiring snuffle and a watchful glance at your torch. Very satisfying - makes you feel wanted.

Given plenty of straw they can adjust their own temperature, but if you have any adjustable ventilation or draught flaps do remember with a climate as fickle as ours you may need to plan ahead a bit.

The way pigs are treated by their carers can also have a marked effect on their growth and well being.

Australian research by two scientific guys called Hemsworth and Barnett on the human-pig relationship makes compelling reading, unlike a lot of research psycho-babble. They studied the effects of the relationship between humans and pigs since intensive farming was introduced. This was a large scale study, although it is still relevant even if you only have one pig.

They looked at the level of fear or apprehension of humans as an indication of the quality of the relationship, measuring it by the time it took a pig to approach an observer standing still. They then split the pigs, on commercial and research farms, into three groups.

The first were pleasantly handled, the second hardly handled at all and the third were treated with arbitrary bad temper.

The third group grew slower and did much less well in all their adult life than the other two, in all factors including fertility. Also if this group were only treated badly occasionally the result was much the same; they didn't forget.

The implications of this apparent sensitivity of pigs to adverse treatment are considerable on a large commercial scale but you with your select band won't as yet need a degree in pig psychology.

We had been to a black-tie dinner dance. Nearly home, I stopped the car next to the farrowing houses saying I would just go and check on that sow who was due and see if she was happy. This was about two in the morning, full moon and scattered clouds.

She was fine, suckling a large litter, and luckily she didn't need any close attention. I picked my way daintily back past the muck hill and, as I got to the road, realised we had company - a police car and two policemen with interrogative looks on their faces.

'Just checking on a sow', I said, as one does at two a.m. wearing a dinner jacket and bow tie, I inferred.

'Oh yes, sir...?' said the bigger of the two policemen.

Looking back on it, it was so unlikely a story that it had to be true. At least it made a tale for their graveyard shift.

# REGULATIONS

There are a number of official bodies who might be interested in you keeping a couple of pigs in your garden or spare half acre. These bodies are controlled from warm offices in Whitehall and they in turn are controlled by Directives from our actual Government in Brussels.

As you read through the regulations affecting even keeping a couple of pigs, including the grey areas in between, in fact especially the grey areas in between, you might well be tempted to reconsider the whole idea of keeping a pig.

Remember that the basis of this web of gobbledegook is the always present fear of another foot and mouth outbreak. We can only hope if and when it happens again that lessons have been learnt as we no longer control the regulations.

So, gird your loins and start by phoning your local Planning Department. When you have told them your intentions there will be a pause and the suggestion that you write to them telling them what you propose in the way of buildings and structures, and before you write to look up their website on 'new development rights'. This is to give them time to look up the regulations.

When you've done that ring again and insist on talking to a planning officer to find out if you need planning permission. They are usually very helpful but busy, so bring into the conversation a few buzz phrases like 'general permitted development guidance' and do they still have a householder book explaining things, and that you appreciate there are grey areas between them and Environment.

Even if you have a building suitable for pigs already you will still need change of use permission. If it is attached to a listed building you will need listed buildings consent.

The general permission to keep animals 'incidental and ancillary to enjoyment and personal benefit' applies only to pets, which don't generally end up in the freezer.

A moveable hut or ark seems to be the lowest hassle approach but you will still probably need change of use. Also, different planning departments will vary slightly in their interpretation of regulations.

In the unlikely event that living in an Edwardian terrace or modern estate you still want to keep a pig, check your deeds. In the 19th century a clause was sometimes inserted that the owners could not keep livestock and this applies to some housing estates.

Next, talk to your local Environment Department. They won't give you a list of requirements as they are mainly reactive to complaints. They will respond to problems of pollution, noise, smell, pollution of water courses and drainage and general nuisance, and remember that if you offend people they are the ones who get shouted at first. However if you have read the chapter on housing attentively you should be able to avoid complaints. Having sounded out things locally it is now time to talk to the big boys.

*They will respond to problems of pollution*

The top of the pile is DEFRA, the Department for Environment, Food and Rural Affairs. This organisation replaced the old Ministry of Agriculture, agriculture having been relegated as not very important for a country which can't grow enough to feed itself. The Department is commonly known among farmers as The Department for the Elimination of Agriculture and Rural Activities, but in fact when you have pressed about seventeen numbers and accessed a human they are quite helpful.

The first thing you will need is a nine digit Holding Number, called your CPH number. You will at this stage begin to realise that you have to jump through the same hoops whether you have two pigs or two thousand. This number will be given to you by the Rural Payments Agency, and you should apply for it well before you expect your pigs. You have to fill in a form and they may need a map of your property.

If you live in one of the EU regions like Scotland or Wales then the Agency goes under a different name. DEFRA will help.

One tip about ringing up government agencies, it usually takes time and effort to find the one person who can help so it is useful to make a list of all your questions first.

Next talk to your local Animal Health Office, this time to ask for your herd number. Only six digits, this will identify where your pigs come from. There are fifteen of these offices in England, five in Scotland and three in Wales. DEFRA will tell you your nearest.

Whenever any pig is moved from A to B it will need a movement form to go with it and you keep a copy in your movement book. You have to keep it for six years.

Talk about regulations on the movement of pigs to your local Trading Standards Office before your pigs arrive with their very own movement form. Also chat to the guy you bought your pigs from to find out how it all works at the sharp end and how you mark your pigs. Your local Trading Standards are now part of a national organisation called 'Consumer Protection and Trading Standards' who don't seem to have a number for your local Trading Standards. However you can get it from 'Enquiries'.

I'm tempted to say 'finally' but let's stick to 'next'. Next with your herd number you will get a medical record book to record within three days any medicines or injections given to your pigs. You only have to keep these records for three years, in case you feel you want to emigrate by now.

To summarise:

Local Planning and Environment

CPH number from the Rural Payments Agency

Herd number from your local Animal Health Office

Chat to your local Trading Standards Office on pig movements.

Pigs have for hundreds of years been fed on waste food and performed a very useful function, but now feeding swill even when sterilised is illegal, as is the feeding of kitchen waste, even cooked potato peelings.

You might live next to a dairy farm in the west country with a cheap supply of skim milk, an excellent supplement, but to use it you would need to register with Animal Health in Worcester and have a permit for each collection, so I suggest you forget it.

Free stale bread from the local baker? Stale bread is now classified by the EU as hazardous waste needing an expensive permit to transport it to a registered burial site. However if you can get yourself registered as an animal charity you could use it, though that might need some ingenuity.

When in the past a pig farmer had the odd dead pig it either went in the muck hill if small or was decently buried or offered to the local hunt. Now they have to be taken by registered transport to a rendering site which could be distant, but with only two or three pigs you are pretty safe.

If you keep a pet pig from some obscure Eastern breed such as a Vietnamese Potbelly or the New Zealand Kune Kune and want to take it for a walk you will need a 'primo walking licence' form from Animal Health, so best get a dog instead? Also if you walked it near a pig unit they might admonish you strongly.

This web of regulations is aimed of course at intensive and large scale agriculture. It makes sense to stick where possible to portable buildings to avoid hassle if you can. Permanent pig buildings are expensive to put up and have little re-use value.

Local officialdom will be concerned that you do not commit a statutory nuisance. A statutory nuisance can be defined as noise, dust, smell or unwelcome wildlife - flies, rats, mice, clouds of seagulls etc. If you proceed with your project and it gets complained about a lot on these sorts of points they could come and enforce their will on you, or respond reactively, as they would put it.

This could be expensive and time consuming so it's probably a good idea, unless you are well away from other people, to go and ask their advice which will be based on local considerations, i.e. people density, urban or rural. There are no quantitative standards and a lot of grey areas and these vary from district to district. It's often a matter of commonsense, the odd country odour which might cause umbrage in Finchley being reasonable in an agricultural area.

*Pigs can get noisy if hungry*

Taking the possible problems in turn, pigs could get noisy if they are hungry before regular feeding times. If this becomes a problem give them more filler in the form of green-stuff. Noise does depend too on the type of pig you have - some modern strains and all the traditional breeds are pretty quiet and docile. You normally only get this type of noise when the pigs are rationed, bored and in large numbers.

Smell causes people's hackles to rise more than anything else. We have more delicate nostrils now than in our more earthy past and rich agricultural smells are seldom tolerated even in the country, except among the country born. Even the fact that you were there first is no protection to a pig farm against being closed down.

However on your small scale you can control this problem quite easily. Keep the muck area of the pen cleaned out daily if need be, especially in hot weather, and store it effectively. Make a square muck hill, preferably on a hard or plastic base and keep it covered with more black plastic. This will cut down the flies, keep in the smell and stop the rain leaching all the goodness away.

Apart from where you add fresh material the surface will seal up and start maturing to its eventual dark, cheesy state where it's worth its weight in gold to a gardener.

Having said that, it might be good to give the odd barrow full to any neighbours who might complain.

It is also a matter of common prudence to keep the muck hill screened and concealed as much as possible from casual observation from outside your boundary.

Wildlife in the form of small four-legged beasties tend to appear after harvest and where there is food available so make sure it isn't. Don't overfeed so there is food left lying around and make sure that where you keep food is vermin proof. It is worth repeating - always keep a few bird proof baits of rat poison topped up.

Flies have been dealt with under smells. If you still get an increase you can always spray the muck heap periodically in summer.

To repeat, Authority regards any liquid contaminated with pig effluent, whatever the percentage, as slurry and the word slurry causes them to chew garlic and make protective signs. Even though you may be nowhere near a ditch you might still be on porous soil over an underground pool or aquifer in the chalk. Other points to check are that the effluent from your pigs is not seeping into the soil near a public borehole or a used well. Once again though it's a question of scale, and with only two or three pigs a lot of this doesn't apply, but it is best to be aware.

To minimise any problems the trick is to keep rainwater and any spillage of clean water separate from the relatively small amount of urine and mucky fluids. If you have a permanent pen you can cover the outside run from the rain and if you use an automatic waterer don't let it leak.

This is not a new problem. In *The Rural Economy of the Midland Counties*, published in 1796, the author says:

> In this district, at Fisherwick, the seat of the Earl of Donegal, I saw a fatting sty in a most admirable situation by the brink of a stream which runs on the dog kennel plan, through the yard of the sty.
>
> The sty is a separate building, substantial and commodious; the entire site shelving from the gangway behind the troughs down to the brook; in which the hogs in warm weather delight to bathe themselves: cleanliness is a necessary consequence. A disadvantage is that of some part of the sulliage being carried away by the stream.

'Disadvantage' to those downstream sums it up nicely.

It would be wise to check you have adequate third party insurance. Even if you have an indemnity against animals, read the small print. Yours may only cover your dog, whereas another covering animals for domestic purposes will cover ponies, goats and pigs. It will probably only cover their depredations though, it would be a bold insurance company which insured you for the pig's life and limb.

A passing thought, if all this form filling makes you think that it might be no more trouble and a bit of fun to breed from your two pigs then the first advice is don't. It would get very complicated on a very small scale. There is a school of thought on regulations which suggests that you ignore them and play simple but pleasant if people come asking questions. This is of course highly reprehensible and could be costly.

The time could come though if we are eventually dragged screaming and kicking, or alternatively in a state of apathy, into a European super-state when we may all have to adopt their more relaxed attitudes to overweening bureaucratic authority and regulations just to stay sane and survive.

Anyone wanting more depressing information on the state we have already reached should read *The Mad Officials* by Christopher Booker and Richard North or *How to Label a Goat* by Ross Clark or, even better, *The End of the English* by David Brown.

In the distant days before elf and safety took total control, one of our farrowing houses was connected to the mains electricity by a bare 230 volt wire strung about ten feet up.

Halfway to the farrowing house was a heap of scrap metal, waiting for disposal.

Parallel to the electric power line but only eighteen inches high ran the 12 volt connection to the electric fence which mostly kept fifty sows in a grass field.

Someone with a careless sense of tidiness had come upon a loose section of wire and flung it onto the metal heap. Unfortunately his aim was faulty because he missed the heap and the wire neatly looped over the 230 volt and the 12 volt wires.

We first realised something was amiss when we noticed all the sows grouped in the middle of the field with their ears bolt upright looking alarmed and facing outwards. The electric fence control was going tickety tock like mad instead of a sedate tick tock.

The first person to check the control was luckily wearing rubber boots. Obviously the sows attracted to the funny noise had not been...

There were no attempted breakouts for several weeks.

# THE END RESULT

You have managed to resist giving your pigs endearing names and decided that keeping them on as huge and expensive pets is not a good idea. The next step then is to turn them, in as kindly a manner as possible, into succulent pork and a range of other delightful products.

The end size and weight you aim at depends on how big you like your pork chops and what other pork products you want to make.

If you start with pigs at around 40-50 lbs and probably two months old you should have a 120 lb porker within two to three months. A baconer size pig at 200 lb should reach this weight at about six to seven months of age. On a professional pig farm it should be some weeks earlier. This size will give you spare meat for sausages and other arcane products.

However, these growth forecasts are subject to a number of variables. Their rate of growth, and thus time with you, will depend on feed quality and amount, their housing, your tender care, and also on genetics and their inherited conversion ratio.

Estimating when they reach the desired live weight is not easy and they certainly won't perch on your bathroom scales. Assuming you haven't come across old discarded pig weighing scales the easiest solution would be to buy a weighing tape. The instructions should come with it.

*They won't perch on your bathroom scales*

So when the time comes it is obviously best to have them killed near to you. This is now more difficult following the closure of many small abattoirs subjected to the EU Directive which enforced full time veterinary supervision instead of well trained meat inspectors. Ring up your local NFU (National Farmers' Union) and they will tell you where your nearest abattoir is.

If you consider you are producing organic meat and wish to sell it as such you have to use a Soil Association approved abattoir which are fairly thin on the ground.

Your local competent butcher or a small slaughterhouse will joint your carcass for you all ready for freezing for a fee, with the joints the right size for your household. The pork will be succulent and what is more the crackling will really crackle as long as it hasn't been kept for days in the chill room. He may offer to swap the head for a few pounds of sausages, if so perhaps accept this the first time if only to compare them with your own.

Besides the joints and chops there are a number of tasty by-products associated with the pig, and the king of these is, or should be, the sausage in all its noble diversity. This is followed at a respectful distance by pork pies, home cured bacon, saveloys, haslet, pronounced 'ayslet', Yorkshire Polony and hog puddings, liver sausage, black pudding, pigs pettitoes, potted ham and pork cheese, savoury ducks, pigs fry and roast suckling pig, brawn and faggots. Beyond these there are other mysterious and more local dishes which suit the people who live there.

The sausage is the most universally eaten pig product but sadly few people have ever eaten a real sausage in their lives. Although there are people making a lot of noise about their wonderful sausages, and in some cases they are quite edible, they too often fall far short of the real thing. The majority of sausages eaten have become vehicles for selling the cheapest meat, the trimmings and the unidentifiable.

Where a producer does start off with great enthusiasm to produce a better sausage than the appalling average, sadly and too often, having established a market, he will let standards drop and profits rise until the customers drift away.

It gets worse. In large scale manufacturing a dismal list of ingredients are pulverised to conceal their origins, fed into plastic tubing and advertised as sausages under evocative names. Under the heading of meat come skin sludge, MRM or mechanically recovered meat which is meat scoured from bones by mechanical means, then cooked, emulsified and made unidentifiable. Then comes fat, usually a lot, flavouring, pink colouring to give that meaty look, preservatives and other additives plus pepper, salt and spices as a further disguise.

Some of the more expensive ones are coarser cut though still plastic wrapped, but then you often detect the lumps of gristle and they nearly all share the quality of losing a lot of fat when cooked and having a spongy, rubbery texture. An interesting test is to close your eyes and try and guess which one you are eating.

**Real sausages** on the other hand are a delectable eating experience, a satisfying delight.

Here is how to make them.

First though, a word of warning. They are addictive and once you have eaten them you will never be able to face an ordinary sausage again. There are a few essential criteria you must stick to and one or two suggestions.

1. All the pork must be fresh, preferably no more than two days old. If it's older, the flavour goes. You don't have to keep it in a chill room, a cold fridge will do.

2. Use the most expensive cuts you can afford. A reasonable compromise is to use shoulder and some of the belly. If you put in the ham or loin they will be that much nicer.

3. You have to use some fat so that the sausages will cook properly and to enhance the flavour. Remember that in addition to the fat you weigh and put in there will a proportion of intramuscular fat, the amount depending on whether it comes from the belly, shoulder or the more expensive joints with less fat. This will vary also on whether it is a lean or fat carcass. As you progress you can adjust the amount to taste.

4. When you make any change to a recipe, especially with seasoning, go easy, do it bit by bit and always make a note of what you did. Once in you can't take it out.

5. Fairly obvious, but if you want a satisfying texture, mince the meat coarsely.

6. Use natural skins unless you like eating plastic.

Now to equipment.

If you just want to try a few pounds first the cost is minimal. You will need a proper boning knife, which you can get from a specialist shop, or ask your butcher.

This is a dangerous tool and should be treated with great respect, never be in a hurry using it and think what you are doing at all times. Butchers where they do a lot of boning out can wear a chain apron (but often don't because it's heavy), plus a protective glove on the non-cutting hand.

Then you'll need a large chopping board to cut the meat on. It should be hard wood and you could make it up yourself, say 3 feet by 2 feet and 1.5 to 2 inches thick. To go with this get a hard plastic scrubbing brush to clean it down with. If you have or can get a wooden chopping block even better. The EU at one stage imposed the use of plastic chopping blocks until it was found that they were less hygienic than the traditional wooden ones.

Also get three or four large size plastic sink bowls, to hold the fat, rusk and meat separately.

For mincing, Kenwoods and food processors have mincing attachments but actually putting the sausage meat in the skins is tricky without a proper filler (see below). The sausage meat will still taste the same though, even if you miss the excitement of biting into the sausage.

When you decide that you want to make more, because a few pounds won't last long especially if your friends get to know, then you will have to spend a bit more.

Get a larger bowl for mixing 20 lb batches, roughly two feet across and ten inches deep. Also two or three large plastic trays would be useful.

You then need a small electric mincer and a hand filler, high volume automatic monsters aren't necessary for batches up to 100 lb or so. Speak to a good independent butcher, explain you are not competition, and ask his advice.

The filler has a barrel into which you stuff the sausage mix, with a conical tube on the end on which goes the sausage skin. As you turn the handle the mix is forced out into the skins. Go easy to begin with else you'll have sausages two inches thick with air bubbles that make vulgar noises.

It is not economical to spend a fortune on new equipment. If you enquire around from people in the meat business and in trade magazines you should be able to get equipment second hand.

To help with your enquiries get a copy of *Meat Trades Journal*. You will find dealers and private sales advertised at the back, though get advice from someone in the trade first, explaining that you want to keep it small and simple and just to make them for yourself.



Now to making them. Firstly, the ingredients.

These are: meat, fat, rusk, eggs and seasoning, interesting extras, skins and water.

Firstly get in touch with a butcher's supplier for rusks, seasonings, skins, trays and bowls who will deliver what you need. Ask your local butcher, having first established that you are no threat to his trade.

Rusk comes in 25 kg bags, though when you are first experimenting your butcher should be able to sell you a few pounds, and this also applies to skins and seasoning. Probably the best way to store the rusk is to put the whole bag in a new plastic dustbin.

If you are allergic to wheat, don't despair, you can get gluten free rusk or you can use oatmeal. Alternatively, using lateral thinking cut out rusk and make a solid all meat sausage with very little water.

Eggs and seasoning. The seasoning is the core secret to the sausage, and master butchers have been known to go to their graves without telling anyone their secret recipes.

The simplest way to start is to use a standard mild seasoning mix. Use this as a base and gradually add to it your own preferences in spices. Do this while you are making small try-out batches - a 20 lb heap of over spiced and peppered sausages is a great sadness.

The recipes below have been well tried and tested on a wide variety of palates.

A good basic seasoning mix is:

4 oz of white pepper, 1 oz of mace, 1 oz of nutmeg, 1 oz of ginger and 1 lb of salt. Mix in a mixer or very thoroughly by hand.

Put this home mix with a bought in mild mix half and half for a fairly spicy flavour, or you could try a quarter home mix and three quarters bought in for a start. Be warned that the bought in will have preservative unless you specify otherwise, and you don't need it if you are going to freeze them.

All the ingredients can be had from the same supplier as your rusk and skins.

When you get adventurous you can explore Mrs Beeton or Hannah Glass but let's start with a basic recipe which can be built on.

For a 20 lb batch, which can be cut down pro-rata:

11 lbs of lean meat

4 lbs of fat

2 lbs of rusk

2 pints of water

8 oz of seasoning

6 small eggs, to help bind it

If you have followed the 'essential criteria' sausages made from this mix will be pretty good, but there is huge scope for variety and happy experiment. For instance try a pound of apples peeled, cored and put through the mincer with the meat.

Sage doesn't mix all that well with other herbs but it's fine by itself, three quarters of an ounce, dried, added to a mix. There is also a recipe, untried, which specifies sage, parsley and garlic. While on the subject of sage sausages, in Lincolnshire they are eaten boiled in milk for fifteen minutes having been pricked first to avoid bursting. Not just any old sage sausage will do though, they have to have at least the pretension of being a proper sausage with natural skins.

For a herby sausage, add a quarter of an ounce of dried oregano and half an ounce of dried thyme. Add a little garlic if you like the flavour.

Another I've not tried myself is half a pound of proper honey and half an ounce of fresh rosemary. For mixing in, the honey could be heated until liquid and mixed in with the rusk and water.

For a really fantastic flavour make some tomato sausages. Add to the standard 20 lb batch one and a half pounds of tomato puree, a quarter to half an ounce of dried coriander and a little basil, dried or fresh. If you like these you can get seriously hooked and they are certainly eye catching.

You might be tempted to try a cider sausage using cider instead of water. Resist it, in spite of the association of apple and pork it tastes a trifle unsavoury. At least try a very small sample first. Also venison or venison and pork sausages look wonderful, but the delicate flavour of venison is very easily swamped by seasoning. All venison and soaked dried apricots is good though.

So you decide to make a batch. The first thing is to soak the natural skins or casings. These come hard and dry and encased in salt. Wash the salt off and leave to soak in fresh water overnight.

The seasoning is thoroughly mixed with the dry rusk and then the rusk needs to soak for about twenty minutes, with a pint of water to a pound of rusk. Just add the cold water, run your fingers through to make sure it's all wet and leave to soak and absorb.

So once you've got your equipment and the right quantities of ingredients weighed up then comes the best and simplest part, making sausages eased along by home made beer, wine, music or just a soothing silence.

First put the meat and fat through the mincer, with a one-eighth screen if you like texture in what you eat. Mix the six small eggs into the now expanded rusk, add to the meat in your big bowl and mix thoroughly. This procedure will produce a slightly crumbly texture and the occasional tendency of the skin to split while cooking, though it's no great problem.

There are nearly as many ways to make them as there are makers, and if you like a firmer sausage mix the water, iced or very cold, with the eggs and then with the meat before mincing. Then add the rusk dry. This acts as a binder and soaks up the fat as it cooks.

Whichever way, you now have sausage meat. Pack a batch, usually 14 lbs, in the filler, making sure there are no air pockets else you will blow balloons and get vulgar noises. Then feed lengths of natural skin onto the spout until it's reasonably full. Turn the handle with one hand and with the other regulate the thickness of the long snake of sausage as it slides off into the bowl.

It's a case of balancing one against the other. When you start you will get some funny looking sausages, very fat or too thin but it is a knack easily learned. Just take it slowly to start with. The convenient size for cooking is the eight to the pound that you see in the shops but it's not mandatory; a half pound sausage is very satisfying.

Stringing or looping sausages is simple but telling how is like describing a spiral staircase.

Take a length equal to eight sausages, pinch and put a twist in the middle. Hold one half in each hand with the middle bit away from you, a sausage length from the middle, and twist. Pinch with both thumbs and twist the two lengths together. Just keep on doing that. Cook immediately and enjoy.

**Curing your own bacon** is looked on as a rare and arcane art, though as late as the '70s you could still see sides hanging from the ceiling in remote Welsh pubs cured in cigarette smoke.

Nearly all the bacon in the shops is wet cured in a tank, but dry curing gives a fuller flavour if you're not concerned with production rates.

You can get a complete made up pack of the ingredients for basic curing from your aforementioned butcher's sundries-man. If you buy a standard pack, add 8 oz of brown sugar to 10 lbs of mix, plus

2 oz of crushed black peppercorns, 2 oz of crushed juniper berries and 2 oz of crushed or ground ginger. You can vary these quantities to taste and include your own favourite herbs and spices.

Bacon is usually made from the loin or back, but to practice with you could try a piece of the cheaper belly to make streaky bacon. Also you can leave the bones in on this joint.

Rub in the mixture thoroughly and put a layer of the mixture a quarter of an inch deep in a suitable container. Then put the meat in rind down and just cover it with more of the curing mixture.

Take out after a three to four days, re-work it and put back for a similar period. Gammons will take longer, 7 to 10 days depending on the size.

After this take out again, rinse, and hang up in a cool airy place for two days to dry. After having done a batch or two you may need to vary both the quantities of mixture you use as well as the timescales in order to reach the desired level of saltiness you want. If you do find it too salty, just soak it for a day or so.

For a black treacle finish, after curing and rinsing place in a tub of black treacle diluted with water or better still real ale to make it liquid. This can be left for a period of days or weeks, depending on the flavour and colour you want to end up with. It also cuts out the salt.

**Hams** are the real test of the curer's skill. If you look in the right places you can still find a variety of traditional hams with real flavour and texture, a world away from the slimy tasteless, water injected substitutes usually hiding behind the name.

With the real ham you have the skilled application of ingredients such as molasses, hops, beer and old ale, Barbados sugar, black treacle, salt and saltpetre, coriander, black pepper and juniper to the curing process. Add the use of older slower growing pigs, taking time up to a year and loving care and years of experience, and this can result in ham where every mouthful is a treasured memory.

If you can delve deep enough *The Library of Useful Knowledge*, sub section British Husbandry, 1837, lists different cures for different counties.

You can also smoke your cured bacon and ham, where lie as many secrets as in any other art, and here you must find your own expert advice.

**Haslet** is in effect sage sausage meat, kept fairly dry so it can be shaped then baked in the oven wrapped in the caul, the feathery bit from a pig's stomach. Kitchen foil will do. The difference is that the meat is chopped up, not minced, and no fat is included.

**Black puddings** have as much mystique and secrecy as sausages in their recipes and where the art of the black pudding is regarded as seriously as it should be, gold medals are awarded to the princes of the craft.

The ingredients for a basic recipe are:

16 lbs of blood (a good sturdy Mrs Beeton-type beginning)

8 lbs of flare fat from the belly

1.5 lbs of pearl barley

1.75 lbs of flour

1.75 lbs of fine oatmeal

1 lb of onions

and seasoning, 6 oz of salt, 1.5 oz of ground black pepper, just under 1 oz each of ground pimento, ground coriander and mustard and finally a quarter of an ounce of celery seed.

Strain the blood, which must be fresh, through muslin and simmer the barley in a cloth for about four hours, allowing for it to expand as it's cooked. Cut the fat into cubes and scald it, and chop the onions and cook lightly.

Now add the flour, fat, oatmeal, cooked barley and seasoning to the blood and mix well.

Enclose the mixture in sausage skin, form into rings weighing about a pound and cook for 40 minutes. If you prick the skins and no liquid comes out they're done.

Mrs Beeton, while she has recipes for roast suckling pig, potted cheese and pig pettitoes (a lovely name for trotters so not as exotic as it sounds), does not have any specific regional pig dishes. A sad loss but considering the vast scope of her book you can't complain. Her footnotes though in the older editions give a full course in pig husbandry.

These recipes and guidelines should give you the basis for further experimentation and adventure. Have fun.

We once had an oldish Bedford van which was very useful for odd transport jobs. The front passenger seat had been taken out for more space.

A cull sow had to go to the bacon factory at Ipswich and my head pigman said he'd take it there in the van.

We blocked off the back with a large sheet of thick plywood cut to shape, scrambled her in over a couple of straw bales, locked the door and he set off.

Halfway to Ipswich there was a crash behind him and the sow's head came out beside him, followed by the rest of her. She then settled down contentedly next to the pigman and stayed looking through the windscreen.

There is a traffic policeman in Ipswich who still has nightmares.

# HISTORY FRAGMENTS

In keeping pigs you become part of a long and ancient tradition. I have to tell you though that in the agricultural pecking order you are firmly at the bottom. This lack of regard is well evidenced by a trawl through 18th and 19th century farming books. For every 400 pages there are seldom more than half a dozen on pigs, but these few are fascinating.

*The Complete Farmer* of 1807 is one such book, citing as well as county breeds the Chinese, the small white English, the swing tailed, the Tonkey and corduroy pigs, the latter a dusky yellow with longitudinal stripes, sounding as if these could well have been closely related to wild pigs.

*Chinese*
(1822, *Tho. Kelly of London*)

It also deals at length with foreign breeds and types, mentioning the African, the Cape Verde and the Ethiopian hog, large and wild with wattles under its eyes.

The hogs of Kurdistan were said to be of the largest size and weight, but the German, French and Irish pigs were 'even worse than the English Yorkshire, generally considered then to be about the worst of the English breeds'. The Bosnian and 'Servian' pigs on the other hand were declared to travel well and to be the handsomest and hardiest in the world.

Going back a lot further, Aristotle is quoted on a breed in Illyria where the hoof was undivided and a Mr Mascal stated that in his day this same breed existed near Windsor. There is also mention in the Midland Counties records in 1796 of a black breed with a similar undivided hoof. None has survived.

Another book dealing with ancient traditions speaks of a Berkshire hog belonging to a Mr Joseph Lawton of Cheshire, which when killed on the 24th January 1774 was nine feet eight inches from nose to tail and weighed when dressed 1224 lbs or 556 kg. A heavy pig carcass now is 80 kg.

*Needed good walls to keep them in*

It also comments on the Chinese black breed which, although popular, were a mischievous race and needed good walls to keep them in and prevent them raiding anything edible in sight.

The Highland or Irish breed is named for distinction sake only being small, thin, bristled down the back and 'exceedingly poor thrivers'. In their defence they were kept on the bleak moors living on wild berries and the like, with numbers of them up in the far north of Scotland near Thurso; not good thriving country in the open.

Another book which is an interesting source of useless trivia is called *Certain Ancient Tracts Concerning the Management of Landed Property*. It was printed in 1733 by C. Bathurst at the Cross Keys, over against St. Dunstan's Church, Fleet Street, and J. Newberry at the Bible and Sun in St. Paul's Churchyard. They sound a jolly couple, you feel you would have liked to have known them.

A chapter headed 'The abominable pig' in another book called *Good to Eat*, by Marvin Harris deals at length with the ancient taboo against pork.

The Israelites were not alone in their abhorrence of the pig. The Egyptians, the Babylonians and the Phoenicians also had this aversion to pork, and this indicates a response to recurring practical conditions rather than one's religious convictions about clean and unclean animals.

On the face of it cutting pigs out of your diet seems to go against all common sense. The animal grows much more quickly and more efficiently than other farm animals and produces delicious flesh. Yet both the Old Testament and the Koran, the latter normally fairly free of taboos on meat, both thunderously forbid pork.

In Leviticus, chapter 11, it says 'Whatever parts the hoof and is cloven footed and chews the cud among animals, you may eat'. Here the pig fails; it does not chew the cud. Specifically on pigs, it also says 'Of their flesh you shall not eat, and their carcases you shall not touch, they are unclean to you', and '... everyone who touches them shall be unclean'.

The Koran too singles out the pig, 'These things are unclean to you, carrion, blood, and the flesh of swine'.

In more modern times the pig has been castigated as a sensual animal and the eaters of pork as becoming sensual too, a good selling point that the industry has not followed up.

Animals that do chew the cud have the ability to digest vast quantities of straw, dried grass and general roughage useless to pigs, and still put on weight. Most of the weight gaining food of the pig, on the other hand, grain, potatoes, anything low in cellulose, is also equally suitable for humans. Further, in ancient times pigs needed forests for shade and food and muddy riverbanks and water to cool themselves by conduction.

A *sensual animal*

These conditions were widespread in the Middle East five to ten thousand years ago and pig keeping was widespread, but population growth and deforestation, as we see happening now in wide areas of the world, gradually brought scrubland and desert to huge areas.

The pig therefore in Old Testament times began to look like a liability. It competed with humans for food, and without means of cooling itself by conduction it couldn't take the heat. It was a dead loss included in a nomadic lifestyle; it didn't produce wool or extra milk and it couldn't pull a plough. On all these counts cattle, sheep and goats which were adapted to the climate were clear winners.

Pigs and the eating of pig meat therefore more or less vanished from the ancient nomad and pastoralist lifestyle and even when in biblical times cities and a more settled way of life took root among the Israelites, the idea of pig raising as being too costly, if not stupid and harmful, prevailed. Even then though there were exceptions, and isolated areas with fragments of the original forests and a water supply still made it economic.

When Heroditus visited Egypt some hundreds of years BC swine herds were considered the lowest of the low and pigs impure and untouchable, so much so that if you brushed against one you felt obliged to jump into the nearest river to cleanse yourself. Pig keepers themselves must have become fairly inbred as their children were unmarriageable outside the profession, and they were banned from the temples.

The idea that there were strong practical reasons behind these ancient bans gains strength from the Koran too, where pork is forbidden though camel meat allowed. Camels had to be allowed, they were vital to the nomadic Bedouin and had in emergencies on desert journeys to be slaughtered and eaten. A religion that banned the camel would never have been able to conquer the Arab heartlands and penetrate into Africa. This did not apply to the Israelites where the camel is banned with the pig on the grounds that it doesn't part the hoof, only the toes.

The lowly place of swine husbandry in medieval times and later in England could have been partly because of the pig's wonderful ability to make use of foods rejected by other livestock and thus earning a reputation as a scavenger. A well-earned reputation too in medieval towns and in some of the remoter parts of the United Kingdom, even into the 19th century.

Other livestock too, horses, cattle and sheep, were associated with broad acres and a gentlemanly way of life, whereas pigs tended to be kept in somewhat squalid surroundings by the poor.

The later Victorians started putting the seal of respectability on pigs, devising on their model farms in periods of agricultural affluence well-designed and expensive pig buildings to keep large numbers of swine. The British Husbandry section of *The Library of Useful Knowledge* of 1837 has designs of buildings easily one hundred years ahead of their time, discussing pig cages for fattening pigs rapidly and in quietude, and quite modern style individual feeders. The converse is also true even today in that in periods of depression their buildings got progressively tatty.

In spite of some gains though, pigs are still at the bottom of the pile, evidenced by the fact that they are one of the few forms of agricultural production you don't have to subsidise from your taxes through the CAP, the Common Agricultural Policy.

Genetics is a murky science but there is an interesting parallel how over the centuries the British have become enriched and made vigorous by fresh inputs of genes from diverse sources.

Phoenicians, Romans, Saxons and Danes, Jews, Normans, Huguenots, Indians, Pakistanis, Poles and Caribbeans among other have produced a complex energetic genetic diversity.

For different reasons but with a similar pattern, an already diverse indigenous population of local breeds of pigs, many with exotic and evocative names have been blended and altered by imports from all over the world. The main improvements in the 19th century came from Chinese and Neapolitan breeds, which had sweeter and more delicate flesh, more meat and fat and were mostly more docile than the native breeds.

Black, white, blue and sandy Chinese were mixed eventually with the Kentish, the Swing Tailed, the Scotch and the Devonshire, the Cheshire, the Rudgewick from the borders of Sussex, the Tonkey hog and the Oxford, the Yorkshire, known as one of the worst, and the Tunback, a Kentish pig with a curvature of the spine. In addition to these and other well known breeds there were a number of other local breeds and crosses which either suited local conditions or which were kept because of tradition and inertia.

The breeds were loosely divided into large and small and of the large the Shropshire was described as the nearest to the original large breed of England. This was the type of large coarse breed mated with the Chinese white or pug cross, called after its dish face and pendant belly.

*Large coarse breed*
(1807, *Longman, Hurst, Rees & Orme of London*)

The Oxford too was widespread, grew to a vast weight and was largely fattened at distilleries. The breed originated from wild boars from Barbados, red or red-black and sent by a gentleman to his relation at Axford near Marlborough. It is nearly certain that part of the new Berkshires came from the same source.

This is an example of the variety of genes lurking in the older breeds and more distantly in some of the modern ones, since this Barbadian import is not likely to have been unique. It emphasises the importance of the 'Rare Breeds' as a source of genes which, while not commercially valuable today may well be priceless in the future as needs and fashions change.

Methods of feeding, housing and veterinary treatment were as diverse as the breeds, though interestingly the principles of basic good husbandry stayed constant. Mr Dickson's *Improved Livestock*, for instance, in around 1808 notes that 'hogs fatten in an expeditious manner in a complete state of rest, and to achieve this they should be given their full allowance of food at short intervals'.

He then goes on to the use of narcotics, frowned on a bit today. The main one used was opium, but 'Be cautious...', he says under the very satisfactory sub heading 'Improved Hoggery', '...some hogs get so sleepy with opium that they can scarcely be bothered to get up to eat'.

A *complete state of rest*

Opium appropriately was reported to be used in China as an aid to transporting pigs from the interior down to the coast. Each pig had a pellet of the drug slipped in its mouth and when sleepy enough they were stacked in the junk for a quiet uneventful journey down river.

In the 18th and 19th centuries food which would have otherwise been wasted was there in abundance.

Distiller's wash, refuse from starch works, acorns and beech mast, dairy food and the wash, anything edible was tried out on pigs. There were several schools of thought on distiller's wash. Pigs fed on it often fetched a lower price from the ignorant because it was believed that the swine were permanently drunk. The knowing on the other hand said that no distiller worth his salt would leave much spirit in the wash. In any event the Navy yard victuallers paid good prices for such pork, though the unfortunate sailors who had to chew it after months in the cask would not have appreciated subtle differences in the original quality.

*Anything edible was tried out on pigs*
(1814, R. *Ackermann's of London, reproduced in* Etchings *of* Rustic *Figures by* W. H. *Pyne, published by* M. A. Nattali *of London*)

On the same train of thought there is the persistent tale of Gloucester Old Spot pigs getting drunk and comatose in cider orchards on fermenting windfalls, causing vets to thumb through their textbooks.

A book by a Mr Lisle called *Observations in Husbandry*, 1757, is full of interesting hints, such as henbane is beneficial and nutritious to hogs but kills poultry, and that a diet of broad clover will make them pot-bellied. He also warns against putting them in a coppice of hazelnuts; not only would their fat be

*...drunk and comatose on cider apples*

soft but they would refuse any other food thereafter. Also there was a sensible warning note that acorns fresh from the tree would cause scour; they were best left to mature or 'chissum' first.

Although pigs were fed on or foraged on this vast array of food that would have otherwise gone to waste, the basic foods in pig feeding to produce the best fat bacon were always peas, beans, barley and skim milk. For the choosy there was even a supply of young pork fed entirely on milk since birth.

It was generally accepted, says Mr Lisle's book that '... the solidity and excellence of the bacon was directly related to the same qualities in the food'. You are what you eat, or more succinctly, rubbish in - rubbish out. Something similar was written in *The Complete Farmer* of 1807.

As an example, the Roman historian Pliny observed that pigs in ancient Egypt were fed dates to sweeten up the pork for the rich and noble.

Although pigs in the past were subject to fewer diseases than today, being more dispersed then and having fewer imported bugs, what diseases they did have had more entertaining names and cures.

The Murrain was described as a species of leprosy, indicated by staggering about and gasping. One answer was nettles in half a pound of flowers of sulphur, a quarter pound each of elecampane and pulverised aniseed, all boiled in a gallon of table beer. To be given in six to eight doses, each with a pint of milk. Another remedy was antimony, it being a great sweetener of the blood.

A cure for eruptions of the skin and ulcers was to anoint every two to three days with a mixture of mutton fat and tar mixed with a little flowers of sulphur.

The first thing to be tried though in most cases were leeches for bleeding, as in the following treatment for the gargol in *Mortimer's Husbandry*.

The gargol was caused by eating garbage and carrion causing 'corruption of the blood'. The treatment was to first bleed under the ears and tail, then give a drink composed of rue, staverwort, hog's madder and mayweed all boiled in milk, which when cold had added to it a pennyworth each of treacle and sallet oil. Pigs being intelligent creatures, probably very few got the gargol twice.

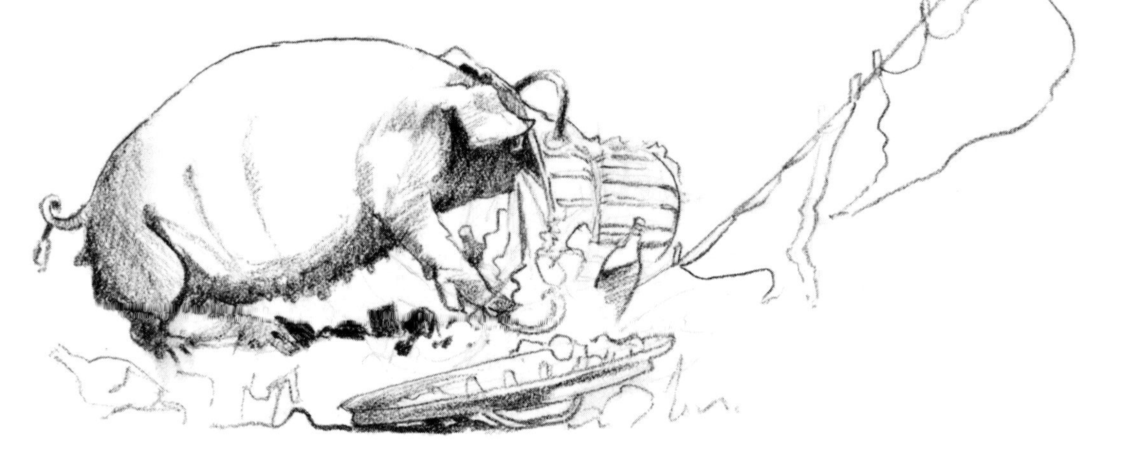

*The gargol was caused by eating garbage*

Bleeding under the ears and tail is easier to write about than do too, there not being much in the way of accessible veins in a pig's bottom.

Edward Lisle in 1757 also has a Hampshire woman warning against stuffing young pigs with creamy milk, avoided by making whey butter and thus taking from the milk 'the lusciousness'. He also mentions the effect of pigs eating hemlock roots in their digging and rooting, where 'they will be perfectly mad and jump as high as an ordinary chimney piece, and it is great odds that they die'.

The treatment for ulcers around the ears and neck in pigs with large floppy ears was to anoint them every other day with a preparation of half each mutton suet and tar melted over a fire plus a little flour of sulphur. If that didn't work, a stronger brew was advised; an ounce of flour of sulphur with two drachms of pulverised hellebore, three ounces of hog's lard and half an ounce of waters of kali from the chemist to make a salve.

Describing also the symptoms of meazled hogs, possibly today's swine fever, he says that they have blackish pustules under the tongue and collapse at the back end.

Going a little further back Democritus is quoted as prescribing bruised asphodel roots for distemper in swine.

A lot of sage advice can be found hiding in older books. This is John Hall in 1756:

> Having named the good Qualities of the Hog, it is proper to mention also the bad: The Hog is the most ravenous of all the Creatures commonly kept about houses. They spoil and destroy more than they eat, if they are not kept in due bounds, and with a proper care; and their rooting up the ground is a very troublesome and mischievous quality. No creature is more apt to break the Farmer's fences than the hog; and between this and his tearing up the ground, and trampling things to pieces, the mischief he would do if left at large would be endless, and all his value would not pay for it.

*'The Hog is the most ravenous of all...'*
(1814, R. *Ackermann's of London, reproduced in* Etchings *of* Rustic Figures *by* W. H. *Pyne, published by* M. A. *Nattali of London*)

He sounds as if he'd suffered.

Perhaps Edward Lisle, having bought some poor breeding stock from Farmer Stephens of Pomeroy in Wiltshire, felt the same way when he observed in his book *Observations on Husbandry* that 'I infer from hence, that it is no ways proper for a gentleman to be a breeder of pigs'.

'Hence' referred to the four sows he kept that produced few pigs, ate too much, lost him money and needed a lot of attention from his servants when he had other better things for them to do.

Finally, it's not only interesting nuggets on pigs that emerge from ancient treatises on agriculture. In the *Practical Husbandman and Planter* of 1733 under the heading 'The Ten Properties of a Woman' is listed 'to be merrie of chere, to have brode buttockes, to be easy to lepe uppon and to be well sturryinge under a man'.

Reading on for fresh revelations it slowly dawns that it's mares on which you're being educated.

Our pig unit used to be straw based being in the arable Eastern counties. Every year after harvest we collected in some 30,000 straw bales, the small man sized ones. We used old fashioned flat two wheel wooden trailers and the tractors were fairly vintage too.

As the bales were pitched on with two tine forks two guys had to stay on the trailer to stack them and they ended up fifteen feet high on top of the bales, where they stayed until the bales were delivered.

It had been a quiet tranquil day on the pigs, with most of the staff away on bales, until a message came there was a trailer on fire down the road.

We roared down the road in our Morris pickup to find our trailer engulfed in flames, the tractor still hitched up and about to go the same way, the road starting to melt underneath and three bashful attendants standing well away waiting for the fire engine. It was, of course, at a road junction.

We never did establish how it caught fire. The idea of anyone smoking was vigorously denied and the best suggestion was the hot sun shining through a piece of glass picked up by the bailer. While we were discussing this theory a flock of pigs flew overhead.

# DISASTERS

This chapter aims to give you a look into the professional pig keeper's subconscious and why he has that wary look and keeps looking over his shoulder.

In most pig empires minor disasters strike fairly regularly. If nothing goes wrong for several days you begin to get uneasy.

Minor disasters can be classified as pigs getting out, getting stuck in some piece of equipment and expiring, the automatic feed unit becoming stubbornly non-automatic, usually on a Friday before a bank holiday, or all your help walking out or getting the flu. In short, just normal Murphy's Law factors.

More interesting disasters are usually ones where you have gone to considerable trouble to make them happen, with the very best of intentions.

One of the first of these was when I decided to start making use of waste food, following the best principles of this book in that food is the major cost in keeping pigs.

The first I investigated was waste Horlicks, which if it did all it was cracked up to do for humans should be fine for pigs, for as you now know, the pig digestive system is very similar to that of humans.

A couple of tons of it duly arrived in 50 gallon type sealed steel drums and we measured out the calculated quantity per ton and started to use it in the rations. The pigs loved it and grew well, if a trifle plump.

Horlicks however has a property which is not apparent when you take a teaspoonful out of a small jar but which becomes quickly obvious when it is spread around in dust form in a meal-house.

Horlicks is deliquescent, it absorbs moisture from the air and when it does this it gets very sticky and everything it settles on gets very sticky too. That was the end of that experiment.

Then there was the wife of a local pig breeder who was deputed to deliver a young boar to a customer in a horsebox. When she arrived she backed up to the pen with the help of the new owner, said 'Well, here he is' and opened the gates with a flourish, but he wasn't there. About halfway there he'd leapt out of the back, landed without damage and was found two days later happily digging up a field.

At one stage we considered improving the health of the herd by eliminating a chronic pneumonia virus. The best way of doing this is to get rid of all your pigs and start again. This was in the days when we were young, energetic and optimistic, a dangerous combination.

However the gap in production left by this process was very expensive. We decided to test the water by buying a few females without the virus, keeping them separate and building up this stock first before getting rid of the others. This was not a good idea.

We bought two gilts and a boar and housed them in an idyllic paddock overshadowed by vast elms in straw bale huts and kept in by a pig wire fence. At least that was the intention.

The boar was no trouble at all, the reason for this being, as we found out eventually, that though he started well he fairly quickly went off females altogether.

The two gilts were an uneven pair, one small and mean looking, the other with massive shoulders and a brutish expression. She became known as the Bedford Bastard, Bedford being where she hailed from. The BB soon showed her mettle, going round the quite substantial stakes in her wire run, heaving them out of the ground with ease and taking herself and her mate for a walk.

After a few weeks of this, by which time the fence was reinforced to stockade level, she sullenly stayed in and with the boar's reluctant help we got them both pregnant.

A few days before farrowing we decided the time had come to shut the BB in her bale hut, to forestall her having her litter in the open. She broke the door down. We reinforced the door with metal and barbed wire and she came through the corrugated iron roof like a Polaris missile. Eventually even she gave up and she produced five very small piglets and promptly sat on two.

The boar was now really off sex and we had the problem of how to get them in pig again. We had other boars full of enthusiasm but of the wrong health standard.

To solve this problem we bought from an enterprising company who saw us coming, a serving crate the purpose of which was to aid the mating of two pigs of different health standards with no contact other than that essential to the purpose. It was made of oak, with green canvas round the sides and top, which we soaked in lysol as instructed.



We waited until the BB's smaller mate was on heat and for a challenge put

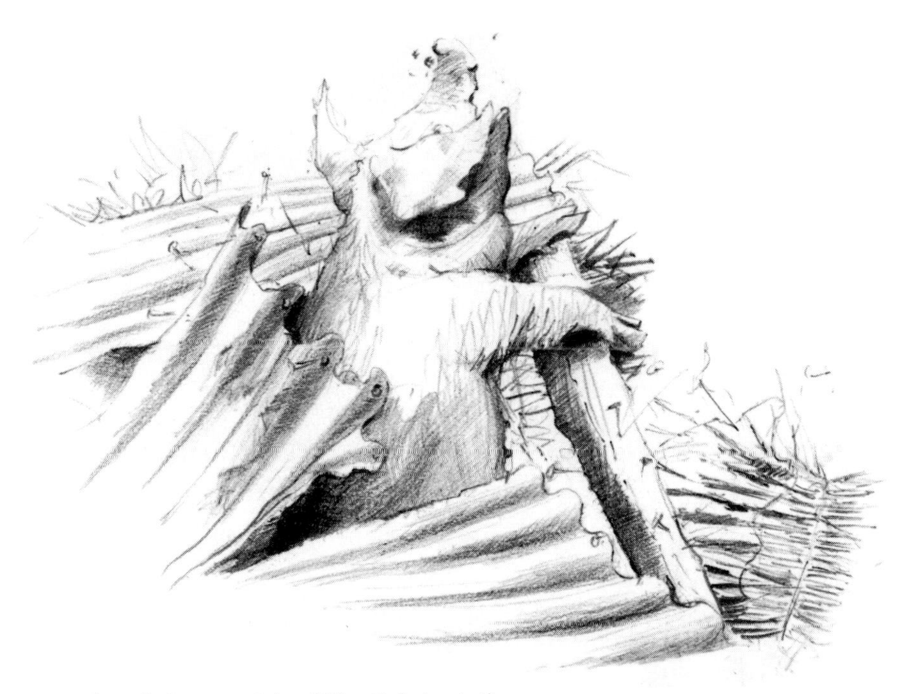

*...through the corrugated roof like a* Polaris *missile*

the crate in the middle of an area of concrete. It took the combined efforts of some fifteen men to get her in, and there isn't much on a sow for fifteen men to get hold of.

As boars rely on sight, smell and body contact when being sociable the boar looked a little baffled when we led him up to the contrivance. When persuaded to go closer he made it very plain that the smell of lysol didn't turn him on and stalked off.

Apart from this, like the lady who, when asked why she'd embarked on the interminable three week rail journey to Alice Springs pregnant, answered that when she'd boarded the train she wasn't pregnant, BB's mate had by then gone off the whole idea.

By this time so had we, and we took them out of their fortified enclosure and put them into a large cattle yard with a group of other sows hoping they would become more civilised. This was another bad idea. The BB set about her new companions with savage glee. If any of them looked like holding her own, BB's mate in a new role as second murderer attacked from the rear and the whole home team in minutes were standing in a terrorised panting group in one corner.

I'm sure the pair made delicious sausages.

Farms, especially pig farms, are dangerous places and there are a number of interesting ways that pig farmers cause themselves long term damage.

Most pig farmers end up with less than perfect knees, because knees are at mature pig height. Over the years they come into hard contact with thousands of hard pig's heads, get their knees twisted as pigs squeeze past them in narrow passageways, weighing scale doors swing violently back on them, they slip on icy concrete and land on them. When they are young and thoughtless they might even try and stop a galloping pig with them.

Feet we've spoken about before, pig's feet are small and sharp so their impact in pounds per square inch is high and painful. If you're right handed it is the left foot which comes off worst, especially if you are crouching beside a boar serving a sow trying to help with minor adjustments and she shifts her foot on top of yours. You then get the benefit of their combined weights.

Many pig keepers start going deaf early due to constant exposure to large numbers of pigs stridently calling for food and the said keepers not bothering to wear ear protectors. This is one of the few areas where better legislation might be useful.

The urge to physically persuade a large recalcitrant pig is not resisted often enough, and many back problems start that way. A surge of adrenalin helps move the pig, which is fine until you try and straighten up again.

Perhaps the worst danger can come with a sexed up or aggressive adult boar, especially if his tusks have not been cut. They can move like lightning and rip up your thigh so quickly that the first thing you realise is that you have a welly full of blood.

They should always be handled by two people with pig boards and a driven boar should never be allowed near another one. Boars however are wickedly unpredictable and even the most streetwise and wary are sometimes caught out.

Not that sows are always the docile creatures the breeding stock suppliers maintain. If their mothering instinct is stimulated by the cries of their young things can rapidly turn nasty. Try carrying a wailing piglet through a group of loose sows in a yard and the hair on the back of your neck will go up very quickly.

A *large recalcitrant pig*

Dog disasters are unusual on pig units. Following a growing suspicion that piglets were being rustled, we bought a surplus to requirements RAF guard dog. The first mistake was not asking why it was surplus.

It was summer time and dawn broke about 5 a.m. and the local doves started greeting the dawn about 4.30. This was when the dog joined in for about an hour.

This was bad enough, but then he started breaking into song any time after midnight in the deep dark. After a few visits by sleepy humans in pyjamas, coats and wellies who he greeted with love and enthusiasm, he learned the lesson that barking equalled company.

We sold him to a man who fetched this huge dog in a tiny car but he brought him back after a week. Having been reared and kept solely by men, when this guy's wife came into close contact with him the hound attacked her to defend his master. He eventually found a good home with a bachelor who liked long solitary walks.

Another self inflicted disaster was caused by one of the periodic three month freezes when an arctic blast from the general direction of Murmansk got fixed in our direction.

A knowledgeable expert suggested that we drain all the underground water pipes lest they freeze up. We did this, leaving pockets of still water which promptly froze and we had to move water in buckets and hoses to numerous pigs for three months. Never, but never, trust experts.

The one real disaster was the fire. After a long period of bitter complaints about pig smell, sometimes justified, it culminated, we hoped at the time, in several hundred pigs being let loose in a field of peas. This was followed necessarily by random re-mixing in pens and a lot of fighting and unhappiness until they settled down again.

Two weeks later, at 3 a.m. came a telephone call, the pig unit was on fire.

There was a scene of devastation, exploding asbestos roof sheets, roaring flames and screaming pigs. A lot died and we were rounding up burnt pigs from ditches and hedges where they had fled for days. To be charitable, perhaps whoever did it never meant to cause such suffering.

Other people's disasters are always more entertaining than your own. The Americans have a tradition of 'hog calling' which is self explanatory. Competing callers are judged on strength of tone (which must be friendly so that it doesn't upset the hog's digestion), an original call (so the ones who respond are your own hogs), variety (to avoid boredom) and a hint of command.

Some enterprising characters had a lot of success with a variety of motor horns until motorists in the Midwest started being pursued by herds of eager pigs.

Also in America, a group of forward thinking entrepreneurs set up a large wildlife enclosure to hold a herd of wild and semi-wild pigs, boars and sows. The purpose was to introduce hunting wild boar, as practised in Europe, until they ran out of them.

They seriously under-rated the wild boar and its progeny. No sooner had the first hunt got under way than the whole herd took off, crashed through the enclosing fence taking it with them and high tailed it for the hills.

To help carry you through any small disasters you may encounter if you start swine herding, here is a selection from Murphy's Law and in its more sophisticated form Finagle's Law.

1st Law. If anything can go wrong, it will.

Corollary 1. Even if nothing can possibly go wrong, it will anyway.

Corollary 2. Whatever goes wrong, there is always somebody who knew it would.

2nd Law. Everything takes longer.

3rd Law. And costs more.

4th Law. Guarantees and warranties on equipment all become void upon payment of the invoice.

5th Law. In any set of accounts to do with pigs, or any experimental data or forward plans to do with pigs, the figure that is most obviously correct - beyond all need of checking - is the mistake.

Addendum 1. No one asked for help will see it either.

Addendum 2. Everyone who stops by with unsought advice will see it immediately.

Have this framed.

# USEFUL ADDRESSES

*Farm advisory service:*
ADAS, Woodthorne, Wergs Road, Wolverhampton, West Midlands WV6 8TQ
Telephone 0845 7660085
Website www.adas.co.uk
Further advice: Telephone 01270 624619

*Department of Environment, Food and Rural Affairs:*
DEFRA, Nobel House, 17 Smith Square, London SW1P 3JR
Telephone 08459 335577
Website www.defra.gov.uk

*Meat and Livestock Commission:*
MLCSL, Stoneleigh Park, Kenilworth, Warwickshire CV8 2TL
Telephone 0247 647 8620
Website www.mlcsl.co.uk

National Farmer's Union (NFU), Agriculture House, Stoneleigh Park, Kenilworth, Warwickshire CV8 2TZ
Telephone 0247 685 8500
Website www.nfuonline.com

National Pig Association (*The pig side of the* NFU) *Address as for* NFU.
Telephone 02247 685 8782
Website www.npa-uk.org.uk (*Yes, 'uk' is there twice.*)

*For any information on rare breeds:*
Rare Breeds Survival Trust, Stoneleigh Park, Kenilworth, Warwickshire CV8 2LG
Telephone 0247 669 6551
Website www.rbst.org.uk

The British Pig Association, Trumpington Mews, 40b High Street, Trumpington, Cambridge CB2 9LS
Telephone 01223 845100
Website www.britishpigs.org

Trading Standards: *Look for your local office.*

Smallholders Associations: *These associations are on a county basis. Speak to* ADAS, *Smallholders Section.*

# EQUIPMENT SUPPLIERS

Nationally, try YELL.COM, 'pig equipment'- a useful source of information on the internet.

Also:
Bidgiemire Pig Company, Allershaw House, Daeside, By Elvanfoot,
Lanarks ML12 6TJ
Telephone 01864 505050, mobile 07872 899527
Website www.pig-arcs.co.uk

Clarkes of Walsham Ltd, The High Street, Walsham le Willows,
Bury St Edmunds, Suffolk IP31 3BA
Telephone 01359 259259
Website www.clarkesofwalsham.co.uk

John Booth Engineering Ltd, Unit 1, Block A, Ford Airfield Industrial Estate,
Ford, W. Sussex BN18 0HY
Telephone 01903 716960
Website www.pigequipment.co.uk

*Reliable pig waterers/drinking systems:*
Arato Systems Ltd, Willow Farm, Mill Lane, Weeley Heath, Clacton-on-Sea,
Essex CO16 9BZ
Telephone 01255 830288
Email arato-uk@freeuk.com

As a general rule on equipment, talk to your county smallholders association whose members can give tried and tested advice. It is always a good idea to see things in operation first if possible.

First, though, the two essential pieces of equipment you will need are a reasonably light shovel and a good quality four tine muck fork.

# BIBLIOGRAPHY

**I have mentioned the following publications in this book:**


A. Fitzherbert, *Certain Ancient Tracts Concerning the Management of Landed Property* (C. Bathurst and Newberry, 1733)

Mrs Isabella Beeton, *Mrs Beeton's Book of Household Management* (1888)

Christopher Booker and Richard North, *The Mad Officials: How the Bureaucrats are Strangling Britain* (Constable, 1994)

David Brown, *The End of the English* (June Press, 2008)

Ross Clark, *How to Label a Goat: The Silly Rules and Regulations That Are Strangling Britain* (Harriman House, 2006)

Anon, *The Complete Farmer: Or a General Dictionary of Agriculture and Husbandry in Two Volumes*, 5th edn (Rider and Weed, 1807)

R. W. Dickson A *Complete System of Improved Livestock and Cattle Management in Two Volumes* (Thomas Kelly, 1822)

Marvin Harris, *Good to Eat: Riddles of Food and Culture* (Simon & Schuster, 1986)

George Henderson, *Farmer's Progress: A Guide to Farming* (Faber & Faber, 1950)

Society for the Diffusion of Useful Knowledge, *British Husbandry: Exhibiting the Farming Practice in Various Parts of the United Kingdom: Volume 1 Cattle* (1834)

Edward Lisle, *Observations in Husbandry* (J. Hughs, 1757)

Anon., *Tracts on Husbandry: The Practical Husbandman and Planter Or Observations on the Ancient and Modern Husbandry, Planting, Gardening etc.* (S. Switzer, 1733)

William Marshall, *The Rural Economy of the Midland Counties* (G. Nichol, 1790)

P. G. Wodehouse *Blandings Castle* (1935)


**In addition the following books have formed my thoughts on livestock over the years. Obviously many are no longer in print:**


Primrose McConnell, *The Agricultural Notebook* (1883) edited by R. S. Halley and R. J. Soffe

G. H. Andrew, *Andrew's Modern Husbandry* (Nathaniel Cooke, 1853)

Nichol, *Bacon and Hams* (1917)

James Long, *Book of the Pig*, illustrated by Weir, Wood, et al. (L. Upcott Gill, 1886)

*Cobbet's Country Book*, selected by Richard Ingrams, illustrated by Bert Hitchen (Reader's Union, 1975 edition)

A. G. Street, *Country Calendar*, illustrated by Lionel Edwards (Oxford University Press, 1935)

David J. Anthony, *Diseases of the Pig and Its Husbandry* (Bailliere, Tindall & Cox, 1940)

Sir John Russell, *Engish Farming* (William Collins, 1941)

A. G. Street, *Farmer's Glory*, engravings by Gwendolen Raverat (Faber & Faber, 1934) - a lovely book

Paul Heiney, *Farming Times* (Gollancz, Witherby, 1992)

Clarissa Dickson Wright, *Food: What We Eat and How We Eat It* (Ebury Press, 1999)

William Harrison Ainsworth, *The Flitch of Bacon* (George Routledge & Son, 1895)

*Fream's Elements of Agriculture*, 13th edn, edited by D. H. Robinson (John Murray, 1949). Also 6th edn (1897) and 1919 and 1932 editions.

Paul Heiney, *Ham and Pigs: A Celebration of the Whole Hog*, woodcuts by Ian Stephens (Excellent Press, 1995)

Agnes Marshall, *A. B. Marshall's Cookery Book* (Simkin, Marshall, Hamilton Kent & Co., 1880)

Russell Ash, *The Pig Book* (Ebury Press, 1985)

J. W. Reid, *Pigs* (Farmer and Stockbreeder, 1949)

Garnett, *Practical Pig Keeping* (1901)

David Brown, *Practical Pig Keeping* (B. T. Batsford, 1992)

E. T. Halnan and Frank H. Garner, *The Principles and Practice of Feeding Farm Animals* (Longmans, Green & Co., 1944)

John Seymour, *Self Sufficiency: The Science and Art of Producing and Preserving Your Own Food* (Faber & Faber, 1975)

Haycock and Hayhurst (eds), The *Smallholder Encyclopaedia* (C. Arthur Pearson, 1950)

J. B. Spencer, *Swine Husbandry in Canada* (Motherwell, 1924)

# INDEX

# ERIC COPELAND

Very sadly, Eric Copeland died suddenly and unexpectedly while still doing the drawings for this book. I had known Eric for over forty years since he worked on our breeding unit before emigrating to Canada and forging a career as a successful artist and book illustrator. After a ten-year career in Urban Planning for the Ontario Government in Canada, Eric decided to pursue his artistic talent with illustrations for advertising and media articles. However his success was mostly known as an author and book illustrator; thus, completing a book entitled *Milton, My Father's Dog*. In addition he re-illustrated Lewis Carroll's *Poetry for Young Children*, *Alice in Wonderland*, *Brer Rabbit* and two versions of *The Wind in the Willows*, one of which was for the Asian market, the other for Russia. At the time of his death he had also been working on a new book entitled *Nancy*, a story of a young pig that was initially raised by the owner's children on the farm he worked on as an apprentice in England. His memories of those long ago days were forever etched in his memory. There were so many moments that he would share with his family and friends of the humorous and intelligent antics of a pig! In fact for years, a pig was Eric's trademark insignia in all his drawings and paintings.

I've always said that he was one of perhaps four people in the world who could draw pigs as they really are, for he combined great artistic ability with the knowledge which only comes from working with them. His water colours too are a delight especially those illustrating a proposed re-publishing of *The Wind in the Willows*. He will be greatly missed.

David Brown